PLACES AND CASES
Environments

John Edwards and Robert Prosser

Series Editor
Peter Webber

Stanley Thornes (Publishers) Ltd

First published in 1999 by:
Stanley Thornes (Publishers) Ltd
Ellenborough House
Wellington Street
CHELTENHAM GL50 1YW
England

99 00 01 02 03 / 10 9 8 7 6 5 4 3 2 1

A catalogue record for this book is available from the British Library.

ISBN 0-7487-4305-7

Printed and bound in China by Dah Hua Printing Press Co. Ltd

Acknowledgements

With thanks to the following for permission to reproduce photographs and other copyright material in this book:

Jerome Delay/Associated Press, 62F; Brindleyplace/Alan Chatham, 74L; The Broads Authority, 19E, 21F (left); Paul Cooper Photography, 62E; The *Daily Mail*, 58F; James Davis Travel Photography, 23C (right), 53F (bottom); John Edwards, 9B, 10D, 12H, 13I and K, 14L and M, 17C, 18D, 21F, 24E, 26H and I, 27J, 66C, 67E, 71E, 72F, G, H, 73I, J, K; Eye Ubiquitous, 51A; John Gerrard, 49K; Robert Prosser, 5A, 6D, 28B, 32F, 34A, 36D, 37E, 75B, 79F, 80A, 81C, 82D, 85G, 87I and J, 89C and D, 92B and D, 93F and G, 94H, 95J; Still Pictures, 6C and E, 23C (left), 40A, 53F (top), 58G, 61C, 77D; Tony Waltham, 48G and H.

The Broads Authority, 16B, 19E; © The Cairngorms Partnership, 90E; Department of the Environment, 57D and E; Evening Standard/ Solo Syndication, 58F; *The Guardian*, 7G; With thanks to the Lake District National Park Authority, 15N; The NEC Group, 70B; Maps reproduced from the Ordnance Survey Landranger mapping with the permission of The Controller of Her Majesty's Stationery Office © Crown copyright, 20G, 78E; Windermere Lake Cruises, 12G.

Every effort has been made to contact copyright holders. The publishers apologise to anyone whose rights have been inadvertently overlooked, and will be happy to rectify any errors or omissions.

Contents

Introduction

To the student...

This book about Environments is one in a series of five textbooks for GCSE Geography. The other books cover the United Kingdom, Europe, the World and Physical Geography.

You will find that much of the book consists of case studies. You should start with Unit One as it introduces what we mean by 'environments' and why it is important to understand them. After this, the units may be used in any order. There is some background information about a topic before many of the case studies are introduced. National Parks, for example, are introduced on page 8 before a detailed study of the Lake District and the Broads. However, if you are going to make the best use of the case study, you need to have some background knowledge. It is assumed that you use a 'core' geography textbook and will have some class time to make sure you know the definitions and the answers to any questions in the 'Do you know?' boxes that introduce topics. This case study approach allows you to broaden and deepen your knowledge and understanding.

The case studies have been chosen to cover the main topics you need for your GCSE syllabus. So you will find, for example, case studies on National Parks in England and abroad, the management of tourist environments, and discussion of environmental issues. Most GCSE examinations either include case studies for you to analyse, or ask you to use a named example you have studied. This book, therefore, gives you practice and examples. You will find that the activities throughout the book will help you develop the different skills you will need in examinations. These include using photographs, tables, graphs, maps, diagrams and charts, as well as reading sections of text and completing decision-making exercises. This book gives you plenty of practice! There are also many questions where you could use IT.

The symbol ➡ suggests that you write at greater length and in more detail. Your answer should be at least a paragraph in length.

Some of the words which appear in bold throughout the book are key terms which are defined in the Glossary on page 96.

Geography is all about how the world works – the natural world and the human world – and is about more than just examinations. So, we hope this book will help you to take an interest in and begin to understand the environment around you.

Enjoy your Geography!

Location of case studies

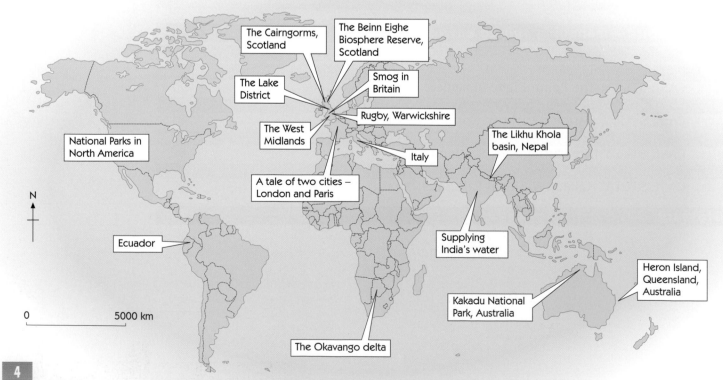

The Cairngorms, Scotland

The Beinn Eighe Biosphere Reserve, Scotland

The Lake District

Smog in Britain

Rugby, Warwickshire

The West Midlands

The Likhu Khola basin, Nepal

National Parks in North America

Italy

A tale of two cities – London and Paris

Ecuador

Supplying India's water

Heron Island, Queensland, Australia

Kakadu National Park, Australia

The Okavango delta

N

0   5000 km

Geography and the environment

What do we mean by 'environment'?

The Oxford dictionary defines environment as 'surroundings; surrounding objects or conditions'. We talk of the local environment, meaning the neighbourhood we live in, and on a much larger scale, we read about tropical rainforest environments. At an even larger scale, we are told that global warming will affect the environment of the earth. Therefore, environment means the surroundings and conditions in which humans and other creatures live their lives. This environment or habitat controls our quality of life.

Figure A Guilin, China. This city lies in the valley of the river Li, and is surrounded by steep limestone hills.

What makes up an environment?

An environment is an area with a certain set of characteristics. Geography helps us to understand how these are organised and work together. Look carefully at the environment in Figure A, you can identify three main elements:
1 **Natural features**: Produced by natural processes, e.g. vegetation from **photosynthesis**; landforms resulting from erosion, transport, deposition, etc.
2 **Built features**: Constructed by humans, e.g. roads, pylons, houses, etc.
3 **Managed features**: The result of human activities, e.g. parks, fields, hedgerows, farm animals, etc.

Remember – a photograph cannot tell us everything about an environment. For example, what about climate, air quality, noise or smells?

Environments as systems

All the environments studied in this book work as systems. That is, each has a boundary, within which a set of parts or components work together to create and **sustain** that distinctive environment. Every component has a specific role to play, and energy and matter move along various pathways between the components. Systems come in all shapes and sizes. A pond, a forest, a farm, a village and a city are all individual environmental systems.

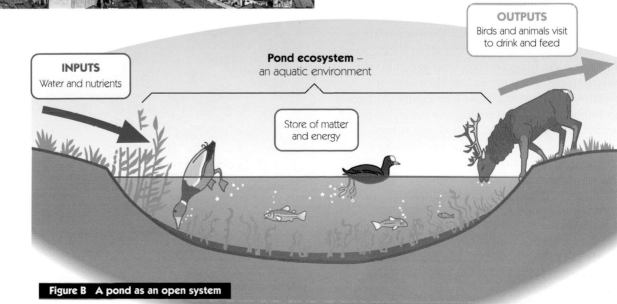

INPUTS
Water and nutrients

Pond ecosystem –
an aquatic environment

OUTPUTS
Birds and animals visit to drink and feed

Store of matter and energy

Figure B   A pond as an open system

All environments work as open systems. Energy and matter enter (input) and leave (output) the system (see Figure B). As a result, we must never study an environment in isolation from its surrounding environments. For example, we cannot understand how a city works unless we consider the surrounding region.

Figure C Up to around 500 m of the natural vegetation of the English Lake District is woodland. Today, because of clearance by farmers over many centuries, only remnants such as this by Derwent Water remain.

Environmental change

All environments are constantly changing. For example, permanent ice finally disappeared from Britain about 10,000 years ago. Over the next 6,000 years, as the climate became slowly warmer, forests grew to cover three-quarters of our landscape. During the following 4,000 years, humans have progressively changed this environment, until today less than 10% of Britain is covered by forest (see Figure C). This is an important understanding. As the numbers of people increase, as science and technology continue to advance, humans are causing greater and more rapid changes to environments. Some of these changes are intentional, e.g. clearing vegetation for agriculture and later building houses on farmland (see Figure D). Other changes are unintentional, unexpected and undesirable (see Figure E). The case studies in this book will give you many examples of these planned and unplanned changes.

Figure D Phoenix, Arizona, USA. The urban sprawl is replacing irrigated agriculture, which replaced the natural semi-desert environment. Can you find any remnants of natural and managed features within this built environment?

Geographers ask questions about how environments are organised, how they work and why they are there.

Answering the questions below (Figure F) helps us to think more clearly about how we should use and manage the world's environments sustainably.

Figure E Forest dying because of acid rain

- What is here?
- Why is it here?
- How did it get here?
- What processes are at work?
- What patterns can we see?
- Are there signs of change?
- How has this environment changed from its original condition?
- How much evidence is there of human activities?
- Why has this environment changed?
- Have humans improved or degraded this environment?
- Are there signs of environmental problems, and can we find out what is causing them?

Figure F Key questions to ask

The people of Sonmiani village live in the coastal mangrove environment of the Porali river delta in Balochistan, Pakistan. The coastal waters are rich in fish and for centuries the villagers have based their lives on this resource. Today however, this **sustainable** use of the environment is threatened (Figure G).

RIVERS OF SAND

The locals cannot remember how wide the river once was but they can tell you that in the last 10 years it has shrunk from five miles wide to less than two.

The depth and spread of the river delta, with its extensive mangrove swamps, made it a breeding ground and haven for fish. For centuries the local villages had earned their living from this natural bonanza.

The river Porali, which brought the wealth in the form of large fish, began to silt up due to a combination of upstream dams and badly applied irrigation techniques.

The villages remain but fishing methods have changed. Instead of using long lines to catch only large specimens – the rest were left to grow – the fishermen switched to fine mesh-nets. This has reduced the size of the average catch to tiddlers. The government has recognised the crisis and banned the 'katra', or killer nets.

But what the government has not done is devise a strategy to deal with the main problem of 'accelerated sedimentation'.

The survey at Porali is part of a £1 million project for the conservation of the mangrove forests on the coastal belt of Sindh and Balochistan. Efforts to save the mangroves have gained momentum because 60–80% of the world's commercial fish catch are mangrove-dependent species.

A community development officer working with WWF

said that, besides a narrowing of the river at Sonmiani, sedimentary islands have started to appear and large boats find it difficult to reach the jetty during July and August, when the water is shallow. Because the annual river flood fails to push the sediment out to sea, the coast has eroded by nearly a mile in 10 years.

She says the river mouth may be closed permanently if sedimentation continues unhindered.

With growing awareness of the links between mangrove forests and fisheries, the local community at Sonmiani identified sedimentation and abuse of Katra nets as its main problems. 'Prior to 1991–92 the fish catch of Dam (one of the local villages) was around 500 kilos per day per boat. Now it is no more than 50–100 kilos.

The huge Tarbela Dam upstream, which is also suffering from sedimentation partly because of deforestation in the mountains, is contributing to the silting problem by preventing the otherwise natural scouring out of mud during the rainy season. Dredging is one short-term solution, but an annual flushing with flood water has worked for centuries. So why change a winning formula?

Figure G 'Rivers of Sand'
The Guardian 6 May 1998

A theme for the book

The central understanding which this book asks you to think about is:

More people +
More technology +
More resource demands =
More rapid environmental change

This equation means that environmental management should be based upon the following principles:
- We need to use and manage the world's environments sustainably.
- Sustainable use of environments means balancing conservation and development priorities.
- We should think of ourselves as stewards and guardians rather than owners of environmental resources.
- We need to create environments that allow people to enjoy a good quality of life.

The case studies throughout the book illustrate why these principles are so important and how they can be made to work.

Questions

1 From Figure A, identify three examples of each of the natural, built and managed features in this environment.
2 Look again at Figure A.
   a Give two examples of an environmental system in this landscape.
   b For each example, suggest one way in which it works as an open system.
3 Identify two pieces of evidence showing environmental change in the Phoenix area (Figure D) and suggest reasons for these changes.
4 Describe and explain briefly what is happening in the environment of Figure E.
5 Read the newspaper article about Sonmiani village (Figure G). Take the questions in Figure F and, using the Sonmiani environment, give an answer for each.
6 Give two pieces of information from the article in Figure G which illustrate how the Sonmiani environment works as an open system. (Think of both natural processes and human decisions and policies.)

Review

- An environment is an area with a certain set of characteristics.
- Geography helps us to understand how these characteristics work to create an environment.
- Environments can be identified at a wide range of scales.
- Any particular environment changes over time.
- Human activities are having increasing impacts upon environments.

National Parks

Main activity

Comprehension questions relating to National Parks, drawing a land use sketch map of the Broads, and answering a GCSE case study question.

The concept of **National Parks** was established in 1949 by an Act of Parliament. A National Park was to be:

'an area of great natural beauty giving opportunity for open air recreation, established so that natural beauty can be preserved and enhanced, and so that enjoyment of the scenery by the public can be promoted.'

The first National Parks, the Lake District, the Peak District, Snowdonia and Dartmoor were established in 1951. Six further areas of England and Wales later became designated as National Parks (there is no equivalent in Scotland or Northern Ireland). The Broads region of Norfolk and Suffolk, although not strictly a National Park, has been given similar status.

Key ideas & questions

● Greater affluence and leisure time have resulted in increased tourism in areas of scenic attraction.
● Attractive areas of the UK such as the National Parks are threatened by increased tourist pressure.
● The impact of people, for example through farming, housing and recreation, requires careful management.
● What is being done to plan and manage the Lake District and the Broads of Norfolk and Suffolk?

N

Key
National Park
Motorway network

0   200 km

Figure A   The National Parks of England and Wales

Do you know?

? The National Parks cover approximately 10% of England and Wales.
? Scotland has no National Parks but several National Scenic Areas.
? Seathwaite, in the Lake District, is one of the wettest places in Britain, with an average of 355 cm of rain each year.
? 400 million years ago the Lake District would have looked something like the Himalayas. The present appearance of the area is due to almost continual erosion ever since.
? The Broads are home to nearly 300 species of rare plants and animals, some of which are found nowhere else in Britain.
? 77% of the Broads are privately owned.
? The Broads are shrinking as their margins are filled by sediment and vegetation. At the same time, much of the nearby Norfolk coastline is under threat from flooding due to coastal erosion and rising sea levels.

The Parks are mostly in upland Britain, the exceptions being Pembrokeshire and the Broads (see Figure A). They contain some of the most spectacular scenery in England and Wales, providing opportunities for a range of recreational activities. The expansion of the motorway network has increased the accessibility of the National Parks. The Lake District, for example, receives over 25 million visitors each year, and the Peak District is easily accessible from England's main conurbations.

Who are the Parks for?

The National Parks are used for many different purposes. Public access is encouraged in many areas, where ramblers may enjoy quiet relaxation. Accommodation and facilities are needed to meet the requirements of tourists, which may be specialised or concentrated in certain areas. Local people also live and work in the Parks. The needs of all these people, which sometimes conflict, have an impact upon the environments of the National Parks.

Who is responsible for the management of these demands and pressures? The term 'National Park' is rather misleading. The designated areas are not 'parks' like those found in urban areas. Although access is encouraged in many areas, the public do not have freedom of movement throughout National Parks. Despite the title 'national', they are not owned by the nation. This is in contrast with North America and many European countries, where equivalent areas are the property of the national government.

The National Parks of England and Wales are:

- mainly privately owned. In the Lake District, for example, 59% of the land is under private ownership.
- important resources for the Forestry Commission and Water Authorities, both of which own land within the Parks.
- areas for public recreation. Access is encouraged through footpaths and bridleways, and most mountain areas have free access.
- funded from local and central government money. Most of the National Parks are governed by County Council and government officials. The Lake District and the Peak District are the exceptions, each having its own independent governing body.
- centres for people who live and work locally. Employment tends to be dominated by primary industries such as farming and forestry, and also tourism.

Figure B Hadrian's Wall, Northumberland National Park. The National Parks have to balance access to such popular sites with the need for conservation.

Parks for the future

The increasing demands made upon the National Parks led to the amending of the 1949 Act which became the Environment Act of 1995. The aims of the Parks now are:

'to conserve and enhance natural beauty, wildlife and cultural heritage; and to promote opportunities for the understanding of the special qualities of the parks by the public.'

Where there is a conflict between conservation and public access, the conservation of the environment has to come first. National Park authorities also have to work with local communities within the Parks to encourage their economic and social well-being.

CASE STUDY: The Lake District

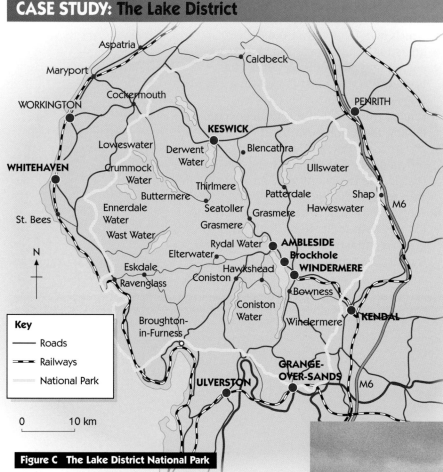

Figure C   The Lake District National Park

organisations combined. The National Park Authority remains a relatively small land owner.

With so much wood and moorland and so many lakes, it is not surprising that employment in primary industries in the Lake District is higher than the national average. Over 10% of the population are employed in primary activities, compared with only 2% nationally. Service industries dominate, employing nearly two thirds of the working population. The growth in service jobs is directly related to expansion in the tourist industry.

The Lake District National Park covers an area of 2,300 square kilometres of Cumbria in north-west England (Figures A and C). Most of the area is mountainous and, although the landscape is the result of millions of years of erosion, it most obviously bears the marks of recent glaciation. 43,000 people live in the Lake District with Windermere, Ambleside and Keswick being the main settlements.

Many public and private organisations own land within the Lake District. More than half of the area is under private ownership, mostly for farm land. Most soils are poor, with land cover being dominated by grass moorland (Figure F). The National Trust owns nearly one quarter of the Lake District, more than other public

Figure D   The 'special qualities' which make the Lake District so popular. This photograph shows Blea Tarn with the Langdale Pikes in the background.

Tourism

The first tourists came to the Lake District as long ago as the late eighteenth century. Attracted by the writings of poets such as Wordsworth, wealthy travellers visited the Lake District in preference to more expensive and often war torn European destinations. A century later, the number of visitors expanded as industrialists made rich by the industrial revolution built large houses near to the lakes. The railway reached Windermere in 1847, bringing a huge expansion in the number of visitors. For the first time, the Lake District was accessible to day trippers. A shorter working week and paid holiday opened the area to the mass of the working population, making it no longer a destination for the wealthy only. More recently, the M6 motorway has improved accessibility to the area. More people visit the Lake District from London and the south east than any other part of Britain, a journey most visitors undertake entirely by motorway.

Tourism brings obvious economic benefits to the Lake District. Nearly half of the workforce in the Keswick and Windermere areas are employed in hotels and catering. In addition to this direct employment, tourism also boosts local services such as bus services, village shops and pubs. Although very important to the local economy, the continued growth of tourist related development is putting increased pressure on the environment.

Tourism also brings problems. These may be social and economic as well as environmental. Management of the millions of visitors is essential if the Lake District is to maintain its special qualities. Housing is a key issue in the Lake District, as it has been affected by tourism. Although the population is rising only slowly, it is becoming more and more difficult for local people to afford housing. This is because of the number of properties being bought up by people who live outside the area, for use as second or holiday homes. Paying inflated prices, they push the cost of properties beyond the reach of local people. Many cottages are also bought up and rented out to holidaymakers.

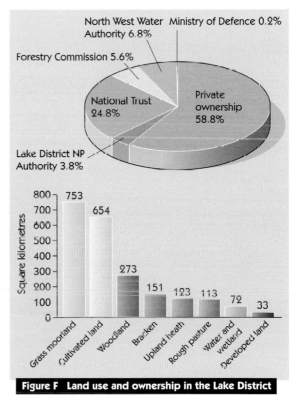

Figure F Land use and ownership in the Lake District

In some parts of the Lake District, nearly one quarter of homes are not owned by local residents. Where development has taken place, restrictions have been imposed by either local councils or the Park Authority. In Keswick, for example, development is so tightly controlled that fewer new houses are built than required by the local population.

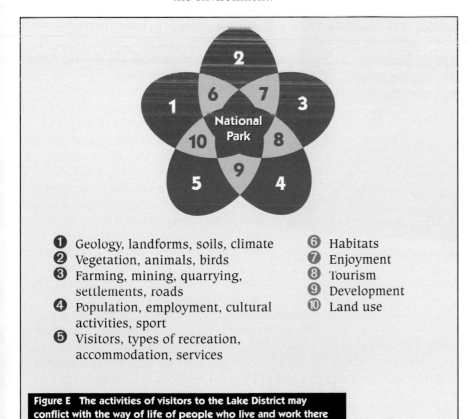

❶ Geology, landforms, soils, climate
❷ Vegetation, animals, birds
❸ Farming, mining, quarrying, settlements, roads
❹ Population, employment, cultural activities, sport
❺ Visitors, types of recreation, accommodation, services
❻ Habitats
❼ Enjoyment
❽ Tourism
❾ Development
❿ Land use

Figure E The activities of visitors to the Lake District may conflict with the way of life of people who live and work there

Tourists tend to concentrate in small areas of the Park, generally those most accessible or best known. These may be natural features such as Lake Windermere at Bowness, or cultural attractions like the home of Beatrix Potter, creator of Peter Rabbit, at the village of Sawrey. Large numbers of visitors congregate at these honeypots, putting enormous pressure on local facilities. Many arrive on coach tours or by train in large parties to villages which are too small to cope with such large numbers. Japanese tourists, for example, represent over one quarter of all visitors to the Lake District. The majority arrive on tours which take in a small number of sites in the area, then leave to visit another part of the country. Windermere lake cruises attract their custom by only advertising in English and Japanese, as shown in Figure G.

Figure H   Narrow roads make both driving and parking difficult

Figure G   Windermere cruises target specific visitors

to increase in the future as the number of tourists rises, and the Lake District becomes more of an all year round holiday destination. The mountainous nature of the area means that there are many narrow, twisting roads which easily become congested (Figure H). Town streets are unable to cope with the volume of traffic, forming bottlenecks causing air and noise pollution as well as delays.

The Lake District has nearly 3,000 kilometres of public rights of way, and attracts millions of ramblers and climbers every year. As with the region's roads, some footpaths are heavily used and as a consequence have become badly eroded. Pathways to the summits of major peaks like Helvellyn are known as 'tourist motorways', and may be seen from several kilometres away. As more people use the paths, all but the most hardy species of plants die out (Figure I). The poor climate and thin soils make re-growth almost impossible. With few roots to bind the soil, it is easily removed by wind and water. Rainfall is channelled into hollows, which soon become deep gullies. The worst areas are avoided by many walkers, widening paths and making the situation even worse.

Traffic is another problem caused by the number of tourists in the Lake District, with over 90% of visitors arriving by car. Public transport facilities are limited, making the use of cars essential for local residents as well. Traffic volumes are likely

With so many people wanting to use the Lake District as a resource, it is inevitable that some activities will conflict with one another. Local residents receive the problems as well as the benefits brought by tourism. The tranquillity sought by some users of lakes such as Windermere is disturbed by the large number of boat users. With tourist numbers increasing each year, what has the National Park Authority done to solve the problems facing the Lake District?

Planning a sustainable future

The wide range of individuals and organisations which own the Lake District all have some responsibility for management of the National Park. The National Park Authority has overall responsibility, although actually owning only 4% of the Park. The Authority works with the National Trust.

As a result of the 1995 Environment Act, each National Park Authority had to produce a management plan, designed to protect the 'special qualities' of each Park. The 1998 Lake District plan is an attempt to solve the problems caused by the ever increasing demands made upon a limited space of countryside. Specific proposals include the following:

1 **Footpath erosion**. Where necessary, paths should be repaired. On the most popular mountain sides (e.g. Helvellyn), this is likely to result in an obviously engineered routeway (see Figure J). Before such maintenance occurs, alternatives should be sought. It is possible to educate mountain users, for example through leaflets and notices, asking them to minimise erosion by keeping to pathways. The number of people using popular routes could be reduced by limiting the amount of car parking space available, and by publicising less well known areas. On the most worn routeways, a barrier could direct people along a preferred route in order to avoid areas of most severe erosion.

Figure I Footpath erosion on Striding Edge, Helvellyn. Notice how the path is visible along, and beyond, the Edge itself.

Figure J Footpath erosion and maintenance on the slopes of Helvellyn. Local stone is used, which will blend in as it weathers.

2 Traffic. The impact of cars has to be reduced, in order to provide a cleaner and safer environment both for visitors and residents. The management plan divides the National Park into smaller areas, each of which will provide its own traffic management strategy. In towns and villages, this is likely to involve restricting access, and providing improved public transport (Figure K). The use of mini bus tours is one way to enable people to explore the Lake District without using their cars (Figure L). In line with developments elsewhere in Europe, the National Park Authority is also considering the possibility of introducing road pricing schemes to deal with periods of heaviest demand.

3 Honeypots. The National Park Authority considers that one of the most important special qualities of the Lake District is 'the opportunity for quiet enjoyment'. This seems in direct conflict with the growing number of visitors, and the pressures placed on certain sites. In order to safeguard the tranquillity of inaccessible areas, development is not normally allowed where it would involve an increase in traffic, recreational use, or pollution.

As a consequence, an increasing number of visitors become channelled into popular locations, such as Bowness and Ambleside. The Authority has to provide sufficient facilities for a range of visitors throughout the year. The inevitable result of this is that the most popular tourist destinations become in danger of losing the traditional character that attracts visitors in the first place. The protection of the Lake District's quiet and remote areas could be at the expense of the sacrifice of the Park's towns and larger villages.

4 The local economy. Tourism is of great importance to the local economy, but over dependence on one industry is not good for the

Figure K Limited car access and improved bus services aim to reduce congestion in Keswick, a market town as well as a tourist honeypot.

Figure L One way to reduce the number of cars on narrow roads

area in the long term. The National Park Authority is encouraging the development of different types of industry, for example by making land available for business and industrial development.

5 Farming. Above all, the success of the Lake District farming community is vital to the future of the Park. Without farmers maintaining the land, all efforts to conserve and enhance the Lake District will be useless. Since the Second World War, the job of the farmer has been to provide food, with conservation of the environment being of lesser importance. In recent years upland farming has faced many difficulties, making it less profitable. It may be that the Lake District farmer of the future is concerned mainly with conservation of the landscape and wildlife, with food production as a secondary role supported by the British government and European Union. The farmers who own the majority of the Lake District National Park will play a central role in its future development. Unfortunately it may be too late in some areas as farmers are now leaving the most marginal parts of the Lake District.

1 Describe and explain the distribution of the National Parks.
2 Why is the term 'National Park' misleading?
3 What are the aims of the National Parks? Which aim is the most important?
4 Describe the land use and employment structure of the Lake District.
5 Study Figure E. Write a sentence explaining each of the overlapping areas 6 to 10.
6 What problems are caused by tourism?
7 How has the National Park Authority's management plan attempted to solve these problems?
8 Three suggested management options are given below. Give your opinion of each option, with reasons: ➡
   a The character of popular towns and villages should be sacrificed, with more tourist facilities being provided. This will encourage more people to visit the most popular locations, safeguarding the peace and quiet of less accessible areas.
   b Motorists should be charged to use roads in the Lake District. The amount payable would depend on the amount of traffic that used the road, and the time of year.
   c There should be entrance gates on roads leading into the Lake District. There would be an entrance fee, with tickets being available in advance. People arriving without tickets would be in danger of seeing 'Lake District full' signs, especially at busy times of the year.

Review

● The National Parks cover approximately 10% of England and Wales and have common characteristics and aims.
● With so many people living in and visiting the National Parks, there is sometimes conflict over how the land should be used. Each Park is run by a mixture of people appointed by the local and national governments.
● The Lake District is facing many pressures, due largely to the increased number of tourists. The Lake District National Park Authority has published a management plan to tackle these problems. Key issues include housing, farming, honeypots, traffic and footpath erosion.

Figure M

The Broads

The **Broads** area covers 303 square kilometres, including over 200 kilometres of waterways. Concentrated around five rivers in east Norfolk and north Suffolk, the Broads are shallow lakes and open water (see Figure A).

The Broads did not occur naturally. They were formed in medieval times, between the ninth and thirteenth centuries. Local inhabitants dug out long trenches of peat to use as fuel. Huge pits were left in the land as a result. Over the centuries water levels rose and the peat diggings became flooded. Shallow lakes or 'broad' areas of water were formed as a result.

The waterways quickly became important transport routes, and home to numerous species of birds, fish and water plants. Some of the Broads were surrounded by fens. These are the first stages in the natural change, or **succession**, from open water to woodland. Under waterlogged conditions decaying vegetation is laid down as layers of peat, supporting reeds, rushes and sedges. Large areas of reeds and sedges were cut to use for thatched roofing.

Although the Broads provided some food, people still needed to keep cattle and other animals. Much of the land was too wet, so areas were drained to provide grazing pastures, the fields being divided by a system of ditches or dykes (see the Ordnance Survey map, Figure G). Windpumps were built to drain the marshes by pumping water along the dykes and back into the rivers. Steam, diesel and eventually electricity replaced the original wind powered pumps.

The delicate balance of the ecosystem of the Broads has been under increasing threat in the last hundred years as the economy of the region has changed. The reeds and sedges once needed for thatching became neglected with the introduction of cheap roof tiles. Following the end of the First World War many people failed to return to work in the area. Recent changes in farming have resulted in changes to the landscape. Tourism, while bringing economic benefits, has led to environmental problems.

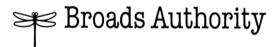

In response to increased pressure on the environment, the Broads Authority was established in 1978 by local councils and the government. It became responsible for conservation, recreation and navigation of boats in the Broads. In 1989 the Authority was given the equivalent status of a National Park; an area protected because of its special wildlife and landscape, so that it can be enjoyed by everyone.

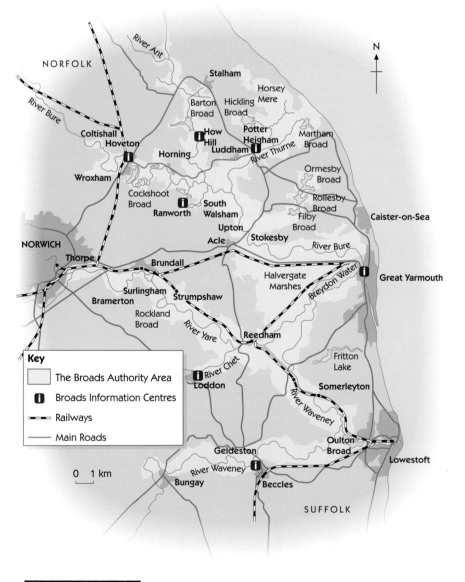

Figure A The Broads

Managing the Broads – a delicate balance

Managing farming

Although the Broads provide good land for grazing cattle, much of the area is capable of growing high quality arable crops. As agriculture became more productive following the Second World War, many farmers switched to growing crops. The grassland was also made more productive by adding chemicals, and by levelling out hollows and ridges (Figures B and C). The result of these changes was a reduction in the wildlife of the area, as well as its scenic attraction.

The increased use of chemicals and fertilisers also had an effect upon water quality. In addition to treated sewage, run-off from farms enriched waters, leading to a population explosion of microscopic algae. This process, called **eutrophication**, made it difficult for plant and animal life to thrive.

The effects of agriculture led to the designation of the Broads as an Environmentally Sensitive Area. ESAs are selected by the government in order to preserve areas of landscape, wildlife or historical interest. The Broads became England's first ESA in 1987. Under the scheme, farmers have to carry out agricultural practices which conserve or improve the landscape. In the case of the Broads, this meant the following:

1 To maintain existing grassland areas for grazing.
2 To encourage farmers to change from arable to grassland farming.
3 To limit the amount of chemicals used in farming.
4 To limit the number of livestock, as rearing large numbers can involve using large amounts of chemicals which reduce the amount of plants and wildlife.
5 To encourage farmers to raise water levels to create the right conditions for water birds.
6 To conserve hedges, ponds and reed beds.

Farmers are paid by the government to undertake these conservation measures, which are checked regularly by ground inspections and aerial photographs. Grants usually cover between 60–80% of a farmer's costs.

Figure B Improved grassland

Figure C The increase in arable farming in the Broads has scenic as well as economic consequences

Tourism

The Broads first became popular as a holiday destination at the end of the nineteenth century, as road and rail transport improved accessibility to the area. Local boats, no longer needed for transportation, were adapted as holiday craft, and new ones built. As an increasingly popular holiday, it is estimated that now approximately 300,000 boats travel on the Broads each year (see Figure D).

This water traffic has caused problems for the environment. River bank erosion is perhaps the major environmental problem threatening the Broads today, particularly where the protective fringe of reeds has disappeared. Wind, waves and tides can all weaken river banks but the wash from boats is the major contributor. In many parts of the Broads, river banks are built up in order to help prevent flooding. If the banks are breached, the land beyond will flood on high tides, threatening farmland and animals as well as peoples' homes and lives. Silt washed from the banks has to be dredged from the waterways, which is very expensive. On many stretches of river, the banks have been lined with steel or wood. As well as being expensive and unattractive, this provides a poor habitat for wildlife.

In order to reduce erosion, the Broads Authority has imposed speed limits throughout the area, ranging from 3–6 miles per hour (Figure E). Signs are in place on the waterways, and people breaking the speed limits are subject to fines of £1,000.

Figure D The Broads become crowded with boats in summer as here on the River Ant. Notice the contrast between pasture land on the left bank and arable land on the right.

✿ Broads Authority

SLOW DOWN
Don't Make Waves!

Figure E Variable speed limits have been introduced throughout the Broads

Conserving for the future

The unique wetland of the Broads requires careful management to remain an area in which people can both work and enjoy their leisure time. The Broads Authority has the responsibility for ensuring the sustainable development of the area in the future. Initiatives include the following:

1 The creation of new Broads
The first new Broads for centuries are being created near Norwich, with the opening of Whitlingham Broads. These Broads, created by the excavation of 300,000 tonnes of sand, gravel and peat, will eventually cover 110 hectares. All material removed is being used locally. Peat has been placed around the edges of the excavation to form wetlands to encourage wildlife. Some of the sand has been deposited to form a beach, with the remainder of the material being used in the construction of the Norwich Southern bypass road.

2 Dredging
The Broads are being choked by a layer of mud up to half a metre in depth. This mud contains dead algae, silt and chemicals which are released into the water making it difficult for wildlife to survive. The Broads Authority, together with a £1 million grant from the Millennium Commission, has started dredging mud from some of the largest Broads. The mud is pumped into a network of lagoons on nearby fields, where it settles and dries out. The fields are then farmed, and the waterways left with clear water.

3 Conservation – the example of Ranworth Broad

Ranworth Broad is situated near the river Bure, forming part of the larger Bure Marshes National Nature Reserve. The Broad is an important habitat for a variety of birds, and is one of the Broad Authority's main conservation centres (see Figure H).

4 Sustainable management – the Fens

Fens currently cover 20% of the Broads area. This represents less than half the area occupied 50 years ago, and the conservation of the remaining fens is one of the Broad Authority's priorities.

The Fen Management Strategy is designed to safeguard the future of the fens. Sustainable management techniques planned are:

- **Extensive grazing**. This involves using small numbers of hardy animals to graze fen areas. Animals such as Galloway cattle and Konik ponies look after themselves, and need little input from farmers. This represents a low cost, low maintenance means of farming.
- **Reed and sedge harvest**. Reed remains a valuable roofing material in rural Norfolk. Reedbed management and restoration ensures that high quality materials are produced, and that wildlife habitats are conserved.
- **Biofuels**. Hay and poor quality reeds can be shredded and used at power stations which burn non-fossil fuels.

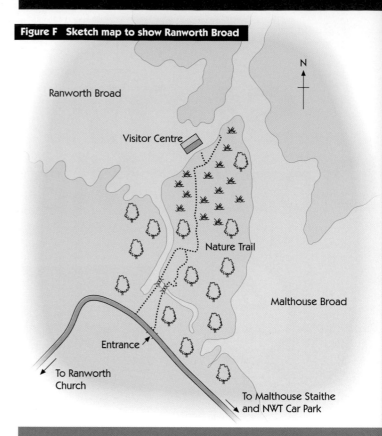

Figure F   Sketch map to show Ranworth Broad

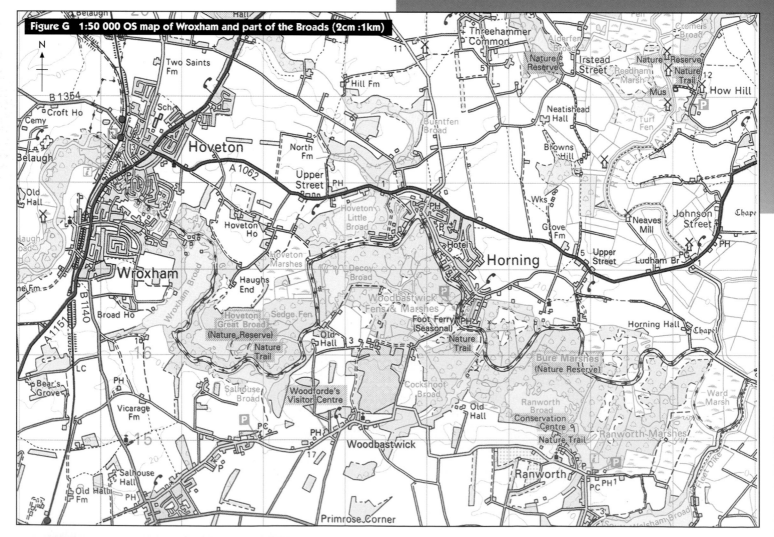

Figure G   1:50 000 OS map of Wroxham and part of the Broads (2cm :1km)

Figure H   Ranworth Broad

▼ Questions

1 Give five reasons to suggest that Ranworth Broad is an important tourist destination.
2 Why do you think that Wroxham has become a large tourist centre?
3 Draw a simple land use sketch of the area shown on the map (Figure G). Include the following:
  a transport (main roads only);
  b settlements;
  c farmland;
  d marsh and other water features;
  e forest.
  Choose a suitable colour to shade each of the land uses.
4 a Describe the distribution of one of the land uses on your map (excluding marsh).
  b Compare the distribution of marsh with your chosen land use.
5 In order to practice your examination case studies, use the Norfolk Broads to answer the following GCSE question: ➡
  'With reference to a named area, outline the pressures facing the environment. What is being done to manage these pressures?'

Review

The Broads are flooded medieval ditches where peat was cut for fuel. The fragile ecosystem of the Broads has been under increasing pressure in the last hundred years. Agriculture has changed the landscape, as farmers drained fields for pasture and used chemicals to increase their crop yields. Tourism has become a major industry in the area, but boats provide one of the main threats to the broadland ecosystem.

Attempts to manage the Broads must balance the needs of different land users. The Broads Authority was established in 1978, and is responsible for conservation, leisure use and boat traffic in the Broads.

Tourism and the Mediterranean

Key ideas & questions

● Tourism has advantages and disadvantages for regional and national economies.
● What effects has tourism had on Mediterranean environments?
● What are the costs and benefits of the tourist industry in Italy?
● Why is Tuscany in Italy a popular tourist destination?

Main activity

GCSE style questions highlighting the importance of case studies.

Tourism has developed into a major global industry and source of employment. International tourism is growing quickly, with nearly 700 million people having a foreign holiday in 1998. This growth is predicted to continue. The World Tourism Organisation estimates that earnings from tourism will reach US$1,550 billion by 2010, an increase of 400% in only ten years. Such a dramatic increase is due to a boom in short-break holidays by people from industrialised countries, and the growing number of travellers from developing nations.

The global spread of tourism has seen the industry grow rapidly in areas such as the Middle East and South Asia. Despite political unrest in some destinations and safety fears among travellers, long haul holidays continue to grow at over 3% per year. Europe remains the world's major tourist region, as shown by Figure A. The Mediterranean coastlines of France, Spain and Italy are the most popular destinations, continuing to attract millions of visitors each year.

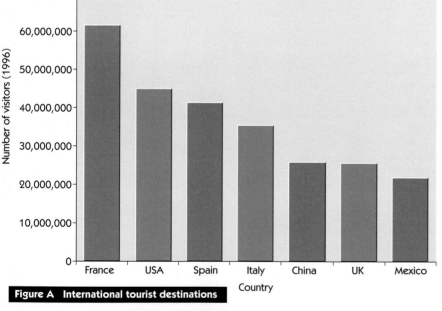

Figure A   International tourist destinations

Do you know?

? International tourist travel is growing by about 5% each year.

? Over 100 million tourists travel to Mediterranean beaches each year. This number is expected to double by 2025.

? 70% of waste dumped into the Mediterranean is untreated. As the sea has a very narrow exit through the Straits of Gibraltar, it takes up to 90 years for clean water to circulate.

? In Roman times Pisa in Italy was a coastal port at the estuary of the river Arno. Today the river mouth has become so silted up that the town lies six miles inland.

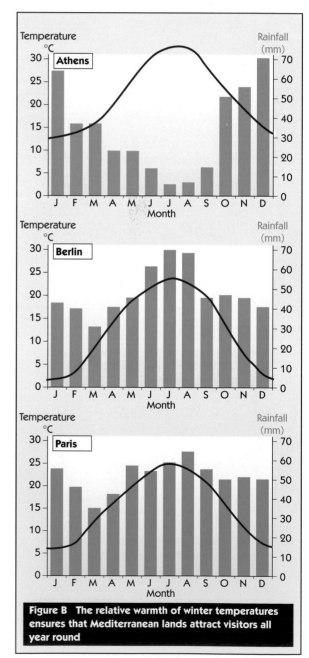

Figure B   The relative warmth of winter temperatures ensures that Mediterranean lands attract visitors all year round

The Mediterranean – an environment under pressure

The Mediterranean Sea covers 2.5 million square kilometres. The entire coastline runs for nearly 50,000 kilometres, passing through 22 countries. The remarkable growth in tourism in the region has been due to a combination of physical and human factors. The Mediterranean is best known for its hot and dry summers, yet the mild winters compare favourably with most of the rest of Europe (see Figure B). The Mediterranean has increasingly become an all year round holiday destination. The sea is practically tideless, and much of the coastline is bordered by sandy beaches. Spain and Italy became the first destinations for 'package holidays' in the 1950s and 1960s, heralding the start of mass tourism. Holidaymakers were for the first time offered an 'all in package' including flight, accommodation and food. Tour companies began to block book many of the new hotel complexes, enabling them to offer holidays at relatively cheap prices.

Mass tourism has brought environmental problems as well as economic benefits to the region. Tourists consume resources at a faster rate than local inhabitants, particularly water. They also create a huge amount of waste, much of which is pumped untreated into the sea. Some parts of the Mediterranean coastline have been transformed from peaceful rural settlements into a string of noisy and brash holiday complexes. The pressures brought by tourism are adding to the problems already faced by the Mediterranean environment.

The lands of the Mediterranean are rich in wildlife, and contain at least 25,000 species of plants. The major rivers of the area have created large wetlands, such as the deltas of the Nile and Rhône. These wetlands attract an estimated five billion migrating birds a year. Only about 5% of the wetlands which existed in Roman times remain today.

The same is true for the region's forests. Only 5% of the Mediterranean area is forested, mainly on the European shoreline. Ancient remains show that there were once lush forests throughout the area, where now only shrub or desert remain. These forests were particularly important in protecting the soil from periods of drought and erosion by heavy rainfall. The forests have been removed largely for settlements and agriculture, leading to widespread soil erosion and barren landscapes.

Although the Mediterranean covers less than 1% of the world's seas, it contains 6% of its fish. Some of the world's most endangered species, such as the monk seal, can be found in the Mediterranean Sea. Over-fishing has led to fish stocks now being only one-quarter of their natural levels, with the result that the region is now a major importer of fish.

Figure C Dry scrubland grows where there were once dense forests. Wildlife is also under threat from human activity.

Figure D Tourist destinations in Italy

N

Key

- Mountain resorts
- Cultural resorts
- Coast and lake resorts
- Other cities
- Tourist development area
- Riviera

The majority of Italy's 300,000 square kilometres is hilly or mountainous, the only exception being the plain of the river Po in the north of the country. A variety of lakes and coastal locations add to the natural attractions of the country, the warm Italian climate ensuring that they may be enjoyed all year round.

Italy is a country rich in historical sites. The cities of Rome, Pisa, Venice and Florence have long been tourist attractions, initially for wealthy travellers and more recently as mass tourist destinations. With numerous cultural attractions throughout the country, it is not surprising that tourism is a major source of income and employment. Figure D shows Italy's major tourist destinations.

More than 60 million people visit Italy each year, mostly from nearby European countries (see Figure F). The economic benefits of tourism are obvious, particularly in poorer rural areas of Italy where unemployment traditionally is very high. Jobs in the tourist industry have helped reduce the migration of people from rural to urban areas. New transport links to tourist destinations have brought benefits to local people as well.

Figure E Italy is visited by millions of people for its historic attractions: Trajan's Column, and the interior of the Colosseum in Rome

The growth of the tourist industry in Italy has also brought problems. Most jobs connected with tourism are low paid, for example hotel porters and chamber maids. They are generally unskilled, and do not provide people with opportunities to move on to other occupations. Employment tends to be seasonal, with the greatest demand being in the summer months. Local employees are at the mercy of worldwide changes in the tourist industry. A period of economic recession will reduce the number of people taking expensive foreign holidays, while changing fashions could mean the growth in popularity of other destinations at the expense of traditional centres like Italy. New roads may bring more tourists to a famous site, but traffic congestion when they arrive is a major problem in many Italian towns and cities.

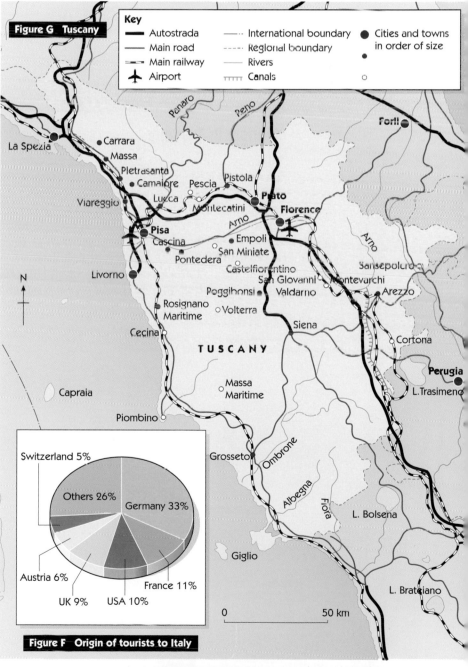

Figure G Tuscany

Key
— Autostrada
— Main road
—·—· Main railway
✈ Airport
——— International boundary
----- Regional boundary
— Rivers
⊤⊤⊤⊤ Canals
● Cities and towns in order of size
●
•
○

Figure F Origin of tourists to Italy

Germany 33%
Others 26%
Switzerland 5%
Austria 6%
UK 9%
USA 10%
France 11%

0   50 km

Figure H   The Tuscan landscape is dominated by farms and hilltop settlements

Tourism in Tuscany

Tuscany, one of Italy's 20 regions or provinces, is situated in the north of the country (Figure G). The area is one of the most popular tourist destinations in Italy, with nearly half of its visitors coming from other parts of Italy. What attracts tourists to Tuscany?

1   Tuscany is famous for its rolling hillsides and rural character. Numerous small villages, isolated farms and vineyards give the region an isolated and peaceful atmosphere (Figure H). With a dispersed population connected by poor quality roads, it is easy for visitors to 'get away from it all' on a holiday to Tuscany.

2   The Mediterranean climate provides sunshine and warmth throughout the summer months. The best known Tuscan resort is Viareggio, although other parts of the coastline also have sandy beaches.

3   Tuscany has numerous historic towns. Florence is probably the most famous of these, with many historic buildings dating from the thirteenth century when the city was the most powerful state in central Italy. Pisa, downstream from Florence on the river Arno, is beseiged by tourists visiting the world's most famous tower. Tuscany is also dotted with many hilltop towns and villages, such as San Gimignano (Figure I).

With the coastal plains and marshes infested by malaria, settlements and communications in Tuscany grew in the cooler and drier inland hills. San Gimignano developed as a main town on the route from Rome to the north of Italy. By the seventeenth century, however, quicker routes had been established and the town became isolated. With no building having taken place for nearly four centuries, the town retains a medieval character which attracts huge numbers of tourists.

Figure I   The hilltop town of San Gimignano, dominated by medieval towers which represented the wealth of rival families

4 Tuscany has become firmly established as a 'discovered' tourist region. Its popularity has grown particularly quickly with affluent British holidaymakers, so much so that it has become nicknamed 'Tuscany in the Wolds', and 'Chiantishire' after the wine grown in the region. Once the reputation of the region has become established, more tourists are likely to visit the area. Tuscany has the mixture of natural, cultural and managed attractions necessary for a growing tourist industry. This expansion has reached previously secluded parts of the region, such as the island of Elba.

Elba, with an area of 550 square kilometres, is the third largest Italian island behind Sicily and Sardinia. Historically, Elba has been well out of the mainstream of Italian life, dominated by farming and fishing, and being best known as the first place of exile of the French emperor Napoleon.

The island is mountainous, rising to a height of over 1,000 metres. Its reputation as a tourist destination has been as a quiet hideaway island, ideal for walking and yachting. Today, with the growth in popularity of the region of Tuscany, more and more people have discovered the attractions of Elba. The island is ringed by sandy beaches and clear water, with 150 kilometres of coastline. The island is mostly wooded, with the inaccessibility of the interior maintaining the character and individuality of its settlements.

Elba is now firmly on the European holiday package trail. More than a million people visit the island each year in August alone, making it one of the fastest growing tourist destinations in Italy. The economy of Elba now revolves almost entirely around tourism, resulting in the decline of traditional industries.

Figure J   The rugged coastline of Elba

▼ Questions

The questions below are similar to those set for higher tier GCSE Geography examinations. As a practice question, you should spend about 25 minutes in total. Notice that the Named Example is the most important part of the question.

1 What is meant by the term 'international tourism'?(2 marks)

2 Why is the global tourist industry growing so quickly?   (3 marks)

3 What problems might be faced by a country that relied heavily upon tourism? (5 marks)

4 Figure F shows the origin of visitors to Italy. Describe and explain the information shown in Figure F.   (6 marks) ➡

5 For a named region or country you have studied, outline the benefits and problems brought by the tourist industry.   (9 marks) ➡
Total   25 marks

Understanding environments

All human use of an environment causes change. This change may be intentional or accidental; desirable or undesirable. Today we talk of using environmental resources sustainably. As Unit One makes clear, this means making sensible and careful use of an environment, in other words – caring for it. This involves balancing conservation and development needs (Figure A). This is the central theme of this unit.

In order to achieve this balance we need to know how an environment works. Each of the case studies is built on four understandings:

● An environment works as a system – a set of parts or components which interact to create the whole.
● A significant change in any one component is likely to have a knock-on effect through the system.
● All environments evolve and adjust over time.
● Environments vary in their ability to absorb and adapt to change.

By using these understandings we can assess how an environment may react to impacts caused by human activities. In turn, we may then be able to suggest how to balance conservation and development needs.

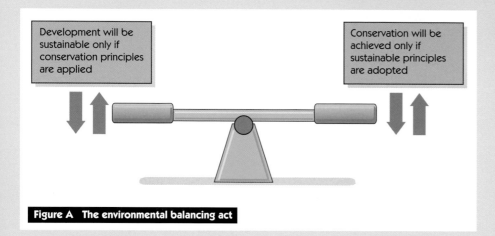

Development will be sustainable only if conservation principles are applied

Conservation will be achieved only if sustainable principles are adopted

Figure A   The environmental balancing act

Figure B   The English Lake District. View south from Blencathra, across the river Greta valley.

▼ Question

1 Study Figure B carefully.
  a Make a list of the changes humans have made to this moorland and mountain environment.
  b Draw a simple line sketch of this landscape and label the items you have included in your list.

Change in the rainforests

Key ideas

● Human activities cause environmental changes which are progressive over time and space.
● Development that is economically sustainable may be environmentally damaging.
● Simple **models** are useful ways of summing up the processes of change.

Main activity

Using simple models to make generalisations.

Do you know?

? Tropical rainforests are complex but fragile ecosystems with high conservation value.
? Rainforests store energy and moisture in their huge biomass (living matter).
? Rapid nutrient cycling is a main cause of soil infertility in rainforests.
? Rainforests are seriously threatened by a variety of human activities.
? Each year, millions of people migrate as they react to sets of 'push' and 'pull' factors.

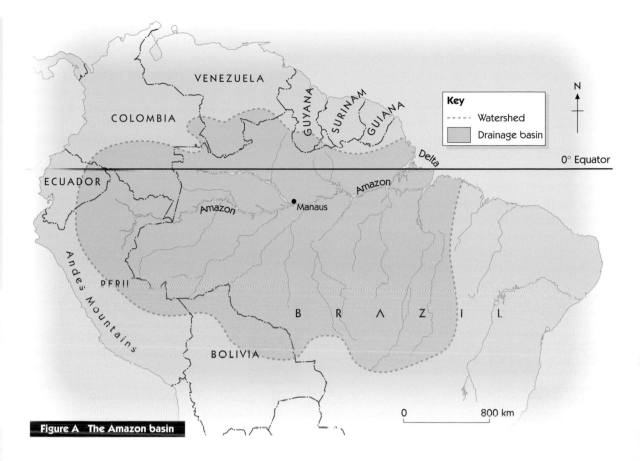

Figure A   The Amazon basin

Amazonia: The environment

The Amazon basin of South America is one of the largest river systems in the world, covering over 6 million square kilometres (Figure A). A variety of tropical rainforest **ecosystems** spread a blanket across at least 80% of this vast area. Scientists estimate that about 50% of the world's living species are found here. The forests are an enormous store of energy, carbon and water, and so influence world climate. They are the home of a number of **indigenous** (native) Indian peoples whose ways of life and rights to their traditional lands are threatened.

The issues

Estimates vary, but study of satellite photographs shows that by 1996, approximately 20% of Amazonia's forests had been cleared or seriously damaged by human activities (Figure B). Despite campaigns by environmentalists and promises by governments, rates of forest clearance are not slowing down. There are two causes of **deforestation**: demand for wood from the forests and demand for the land on which the forest grows.

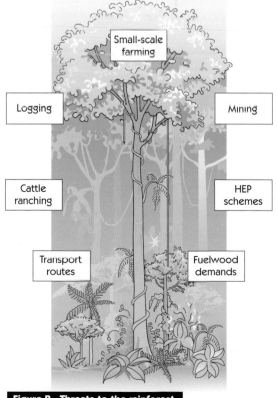

Figure B   Threats to the rainforest

Understanding the issues

Forests are cleared for several reasons, and conditions vary from place to place. This means that understanding what is happening is not easy. We need to look for simple ways of showing how changes progress, and what happens to the environment. One method is to make generalisations by the use of simple models.

Two examples from Brazil show how this can be done at different scales. The first takes the issue of fuelwood at the national scale (Figure C). Fuelwood, i.e. wood burned as a source of energy, provides about 12% of Brazil's energy supply. The most densely populated regions are in the south and east of the country. As a result, deforestation has been most severe in these regions. Over time, demand has continued to grow, and the zone of wood supply is pushing ever further into the Amazon basin. Figure C is a simple model which sums up this process.

The second example is at the regional scale, using the State of Para, in north-east Brazil. As in so much of the Amazon basin, **timber extraction** (logging) is widespread in Para. When a district is first opened up, the timber mills tend to be small, low-tech and draw materials from a local area. Over time however, this changes, and environmental impacts become more severe. The model in Figure D sums up this process in one simple diagram.

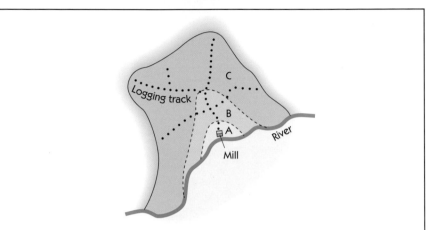

Small mill Small catchment area

Phase 1 A small, low-tech mill is set up. A few commercially valuable hardwood species are felled and dragged from the nearby forest (Zone A). About 80% of the trees in the 'harvested' area remain. The mill has low capacity and so processed timber volume is small.

Phase 2 Valuable hardwood species in Zone A become scarce, and hardwood logging extends into Zone B. New milling equipment is introduced, and clear-felling spreads across Zone A. This supplies wood for making pulp. Logging tracks penetrate the forest.

Phase 3 Little forest remains in Zone A. Clear-felling extends across Zone B. More logging tracks push into Zone C where the selective hardwood logging takes place first. Because of increased distances, costs rise. So, modern, more efficient milling equipment is introduced to reduce production costs. But this new mill has greater capacity and demands on forest resources increase.

Phase 4 Plantations of fast-growing softwood species appear in Zone A. These maintain supplies to the new, larger pulpwood mills. In time, these will spread into Zone B. Selective hardwood logging continues in Zone C, with more logging tracks disturbing the forest.

Large mill Large catchment area

Figure D   Environmental impacts of logging

Key
- Shortage: Forest resources already severely reduced
- Declining reserves: A shortage is likely early in the twenty first century
- Satisfactory reserves: Enough forest resources for the future

Figure C   A model of fuelwood demand in Brazil

▼ Questions

1. Use Figure C to describe the threat to Brazil's rainforests caused by the huge demand for fuelwood. (You may find an atlas useful to locate the main cities and centres of demand.)
2. Using Figure D, give two differences between the environmental impacts of timber extraction in Phases 1 and 4.
3. Suggest a possible 'Phase 5' for the logging industry in Para. For example, will the kind of timber extraction change? Might the milling close down, and why? ◆

CASE STUDY: Ecuador

This case study reduces the scale to that of the individual farm unit. Figure F summarises what is happening in the region of Ecuador that lies within the Amazon basin. During the past 25 years, a growing tide of migrants has been moving into the forests. They are mainly families who clear relatively small areas in order to make a living. Once again, their impacts on the forests are progressive, i.e. change and spread over time.

Ecuador's rainforests are well-known for their **biodiversity**. Scientists believe there are more species per hectare than in Brazil. Yet each year during the 1990s, Ecuador has been losing 1.8% of these rich forests. This is the highest deforestation rate of any of the countries in the Amazon basin. A conversation between a journalist and a university geographer explains what is happening (Figure E).

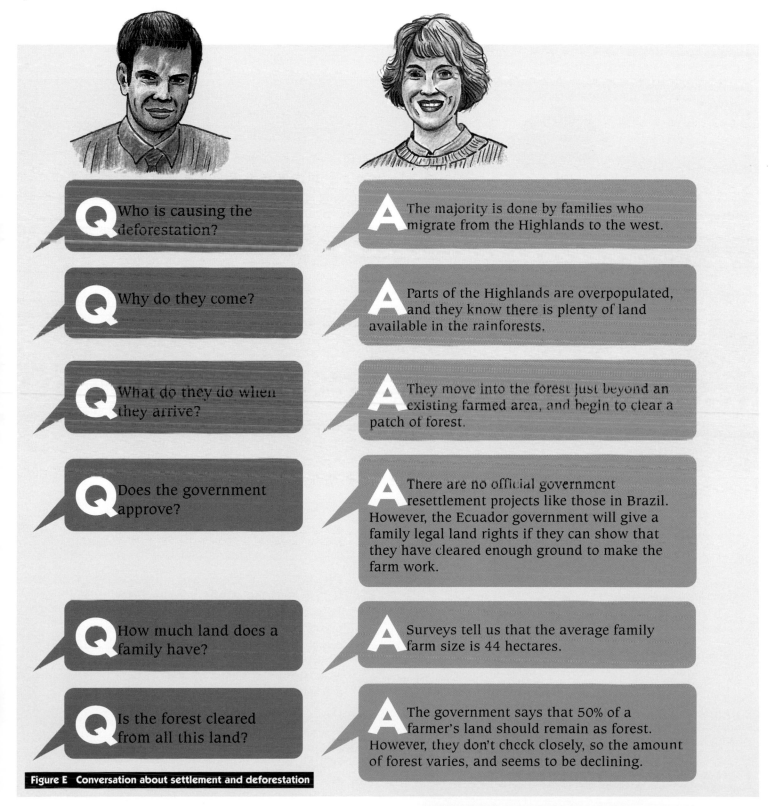

Q Who is causing the deforestation?

A The majority is done by families who migrate from the Highlands to the west.

Q Why do they come?

A Parts of the Highlands are overpopulated, and they know there is plenty of land available in the rainforests.

Q What do they do when they arrive?

A They move into the forest just beyond an existing farmed area, and begin to clear a patch of forest.

Q Does the government approve?

A There are no official government resettlement projects like those in Brazil. However, the Ecuador government will give a family legal land rights if they can show that they have cleared enough ground to make the farm work.

Q How much land does a family have?

A Surveys tell us that the average family farm size is 44 hectares.

Q Is the forest cleared from all this land?

A The government says that 50% of a farmer's land should remain as forest. However, they don't check closely, so the amount of forest varies, and seems to be declining.

Figure E Conversation about settlement and deforestation

Farming and the environment

Not all settlers succeed, but failure rates are much lower than in Brazil. For example, in Rondonia State, Brazil, where there have been massive government **resettlement** projects, up to one-third of all migrant farmers move on again within five years. In Ecuador, the failure rate is no more than one-in-ten. Two factors influence this relatively low failure rate: most soils are more fertile than in Brazil, and the majority of settlers have some farming experience in the region they have moved from.

A successful farm tends to progress through three phases, as the family adjusts to the new environment (Figure F). Notice how two opposing trends run alongside each other: as the commercial element of the farm (crops and animals for sale) increases, so the proportion of land remaining under forest decreases. In 1995, on average, over 50% of a farm was still forested. But remember that these figures are averages, taken from farms in all three phases of development. Therefore, forest area will vary widely.

Phase 1
'Let's start with what we know'
This is a coping phase. A small area is cleared to grow food crops, using techniques learned in the region the family came from. 'Slash-and-burn' and 'Slash-and-mulch' techniques are used. The cut vegetation is either burned or is left to decompose (mulch) to add nutrients to the soil.

Phase 2
'Let's try this'
This is an experimenting phase. New methods and crops are tried, including cash crops especially coffee. More land is cleared to make space for the cash crops. With money from selling produce, more farmers buy chain saws. This allows more deforestation.

Phase 3
'Let's choose what works best'
This is an adapting and adopting phase. The family uses their experience to choose the combination of crops and animals which suits them and the local environment best. Cattle numbers are increased because of their food and market value. Coffee is the main cash crop.

Figure F   A model to show the phases of a successful farm

Is the system sustainable?

The following list sums up the situation in the mid-1990s:

- The 1995 land use figures (Figure G) tell us that 56% of the land taken up by settlers was still under forest.
- Cattle rearing causes most environmental impact, as about one hectare is needed for each head of cattle.
- In 1995 the average size of a herd on a farm was eight cattle.
- Research carried out between 1990 and 1995 showed that the most successful farms – those making most money – had more cattle and larger areas growing coffee.
- The Ecuador government uses the rainforest region as a 'frontier zone' with plenty of space where landless families can settle. For the government this informal movement is less expensive than official resettlement projects. It is also easier than major **land reform** programmes which take land from rich landowners and allocate it to landless families.
- For the farmer, there are three factors of production: land, which is plentiful; labour, which may be scarce unless the family is large; capital, which is scarce. This is a type of balance sheet. It tells us:
  i) the farmer is likely to 'spend' (use) freely on land but try to save on the use of labour and capital;
  ii) large families have economic value;
  iii) the farmer is likely to concentrate on the products which bring in most money, e.g. cattle and coffee.
- The Ecuador government is trying to reduce the rate of population growth throughout the country.

▼ Questions

1 Give one 'push' factor and one 'pull' factor which is causing migration into Ecuador's rainforests.
2 What is the policy of the Ecuador government towards the migration?
3 What had been the effect upon the rainforest by 1995?
4 Give two reasons why Phase 1 of the settlement model (Figure F) may be the most difficult for migrant families.
5 Using Figure F, suggest two differences between a farm in Phase 1 and a farm in Phase 3 of the model. Explain these differences.
6 Use Figure F and read the section, 'Is the system sustainable?'
   a Describe and explain briefly what you think is likely to happen to the rainforest during the next ten years.
   b What may be the environmental impact of the following change in the balance between the factors of production on a farm: the family gets larger and the farmer is able to buy more equipment?
7 Are the policies of the Ecuador government helping or hindering environmental sustainability? Give your reasons. ➡
8 Suggest a possible 'Phase 4' for the model in Figure F.
9 Use the information in this case study to discuss this hypothesis:
   'The development processes taking place in the rainforests of Ecuador are economically and socially sustainable but environmentally non-sustainable.' ➡

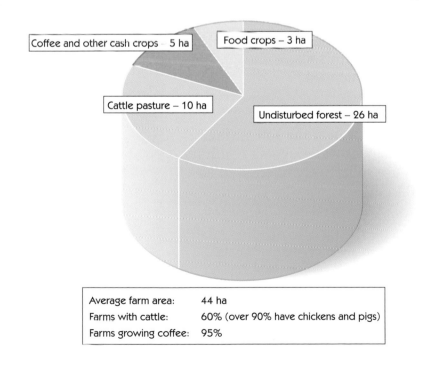

Average farm area:	44 ha
Farms with cattle:	60% (over 90% have chickens and pigs)
Farms growing coffee:	95%

Review

- The rainforests of Amazonia are valuable ecologically and economically.
- These forests are increasingly threatened by a variety of human activities.
- As farmers become more successful economically, environmental impacts may increase. This may affect long-term sustainability.
- The impacts of deforestation change over time. We can sum up this progression by using simple models.

Figure G   Land use in settled areas of Ecuador's rainforests 1995

Wetland environments

Figure A   The tundra wetlands, crossed by braided streams. Denali National Park, Alaska, USA.

Key ideas

● Wetlands are diverse and productive environments.
● Wetlands have several important environmental functions.
● Wetland environments are attractive for human activities and have high economic value.
● Wetlands have high conservation values.

Main activity

Using the systems approach to study an environment.

What do we mean by 'wetlands'?

Wetlands are defined in several ways. Here are three useful definitions:

> 'Wetlands are those areas where land and water meet.'
>
> (Crace.J. Guardian Education, 6 September 1996, p.10.)

> 'Wetlands are lands with soils that are periodically flooded.'
>
> (Williams. M. [ed], Wetlands: A threatened landscape Blackwell, 1990, p.1.)

> 'Wherever… the water-table is at or near the soil surface for much of the year, the consequent waterlogging results in plant communities which are collectively referred to as wetlands.'
>
> (Moore D M Green Planet, CUP, 1982, p.191.)

These definitions give us several clues to understanding wetlands:
● **Location**: they develop along the boundary between land (terrestrial) and water (aquatic) ecosystems.
● **Ecology**: the plants and animals which live there are adapted to waterlogged conditions.
● **Soils**: these vary according to how often and for how long they are waterlogged.

Do you know?

? Wetlands are found across a wide range of latitudes and altitudes throughout the world.
? Population densities vary from very low, e.g. the **tundra** in northern Canada, to very high, e.g. river deltas in Bangladesh and Vietnam.
? Some of the world's best and profitable farming is found on drained wetlands such as the polders of the Netherlands.
? Wetlands attract people, but also threaten them because of flood dangers, e.g. in spring 1998, serious flooding in a number of river valleys in eastern England; in summer 1998 several million Chinese had to leave their homes when the river Yangtse flooded.

Under natural conditions, wetlands cover 6% of the world's land surface and are found in most major climatic zones. For example, around 25% of the global total stretch across the tundra of Alaska, northern Canada and Siberia (Figure A); another 25% occur within the tropics, e.g. mangrove swamps. As a result, the general term 'wetland' includes a wide variety of environments. In the British Isles this variety can be seen by the names we use: mires, bogs, fens, carrs, marshes, swamps. These names also refer to the key understanding that wetlands are dynamic environments – they change over time (Figure B). There are several ways we can group these different environments into major types, e.g. by **latitude** (tropical, mid-latitude, high latitude); by **altitude** (low level, montane); by **location** (coastal, inland) see Figure C.

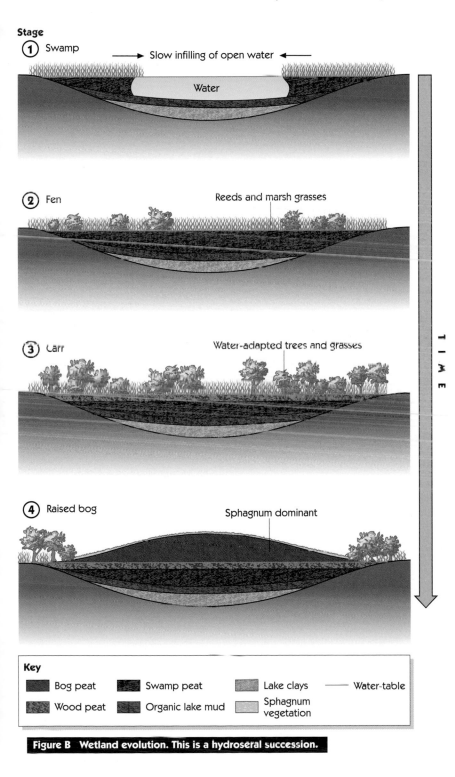

Stage
1. Swamp
2. Fen — Reeds and marsh grasses
3. Carr — Water-adapted trees and grasses
4. Raised bog — Sphagnum dominant

Slow infilling of open water — Water

Key

| Bog peat | Swamp peat | Lake clays | — Water-table |
| Wood peat | Organic lake mud | Sphagnum vegetation | |

Figure B Wetland evolution. This is a hydroseral succession.

Wetlands at work

Wetlands have several important functions:

Physical
- Coastal protection, e.g. 50% of wave energy is absorbed within the first three metres of a coastal marsh.
- Flood control, e.g. low lying water meadows act as temporary stores for river flood water. This reduces flood risk farther downstream.
- Refilling (recharging) groundwater stores as water **percolates** slowly downwards.
- Sediment trapping, causes the addition of fertile sediments and organic debris.

Chemical
- Water is purified by filtering through the vegetation and sediments. This removes pollutants and **toxic** wastes from the water.

Biological
- Many wetlands are highly productive ecosystems, with considerable biodiversity; nurseries for young fish and other aquatic species; vital habitats for wildlife, e.g. where migrating birds can rest and feed.

Coastal	Inland
Estuary	Floodplain and bottomland
Delta	Delta (inland drainage basin)
Intertidal flats	Lowland fens/carr
Sand-bar and lagoon marsh	Upland blanket bog
Mangrove swamp	Raised bog
Coral reef and atoll	Tundra (upland, lowland, coastal)
	Glaciated pothole country
	Shallow pond and lake fringe

Figure C Wetland types

Figure D Mission Bay Park, San Diego, California, USA, created by infilling a lagoon and marsh. The Pacific Ocean lies beyond the sand bar along the left of the photo.

Threats to wetlands

Scientists estimate that if we exclude the vast wetlands of the cold, remote tundra, at least 50% of the world's wetlands have disappeared or been seriously damaged. Wetlands and the space they occupy have become very attractive to humans: people like to live and play along coastlines (Figure D). Figure D shows one of a series of saltmarsh inlets along the coast of southern California. Today it has been drained and infilled to become a high quality recreation area for local people and tourists. It includes the famous Sea World theme park. Migratory birds travelling the Pacific Flyway between Alaska and Mexico, have lost a rich resting and feeding ground.

Farmers in **MEDCs** (More Economically Developed Countries) and **LEDCs** (Less Economically Developed Countries) have been attracted to the fertile soils of many lowland wetlands. In England, less than 5% of East Anglia's natural fens remain.

In the USA 300,000 acres of wetland are being lost each year to urban growth and land reclamation (Figure E). Wetlands are also threatened by pollution, e.g. acid rain, oil slicks and chemicals from intensive agriculture.

▼ Questions

1 Look at Figure B.
  a In one sentence, describe the environment in Stage 1.
  b For each of Stages 2, 3 and 4 give one important change from the preceding phase.
  c Explain why the wetland of Stage 4 is sometimes called a 'raised bog'.

2 Look at the photo of Mission Bay (Figure D).
  a What importance did the natural saltmarsh have?
  b What advantages have local people gained?
  c Suggest two ways in which San Diego gets economic benefits from the Mission Bay development.

3 The Mississippi Delta is changing (Figure E). Give one example of:
  a loss to the environment;
  b benefit to the economy;
  c advantages for local people.

4 Use the Mission Bay and Mississippi Delta examples to support the claim that environmental losses may be balanced by economic and social gains.

◀ A specialised environment
The tupelo and black cypress trees of the bottomland swamps have adapted to the waterlogged conditions. For example, they have evolved air roots, which grow above the water level to draw in the oxygen the trees need.

▶ A rich, diverse environment
The river discharges its water and sediment across the flat delta surface. This is a species-rich ecosystem, with the grasses, reeds, marsh plants, shrubs and trees supporting a range of fish, animal and bird species.

▲ A productive environment
When drained, the fertile soils become very productive cropland, giving some of the highest yields in the USA. This is a highly managed environment, farmed intensively for sugar, rice and cotton.

▶ A valued environment
More than one-half of the delta's natural wetlands have disappeared. Many remaining areas are protected. Here, in Noxubee National Wildlife Refuge, conservation is given priority. The wetlands are also popular for recreation.

Figure E   The Mississippi Delta: A subtropical wetland

CASE STUDY: The Okavango Delta

A wetland is an environmental system. This means that it is made up of a set of components which work together, and depend on each other. However, like all environmental systems, a wetland is connected with surrounding systems. It is an open system. This case study of the Okavango Delta in Botswana in southern Africa (Figure F) shows how an open system works. The materials focus on three key questions:

● How does the delta wetland work under natural conditions?
● What impacts are human activities having on the wetland ecosystem?
● Are human activities affecting the sustainability of the delta environment?

Water – the vital input, throughput and output

The Okavango Delta is an extensive, complex wetland, about the size of Wales (Figure F). It is a huge water store, occurring in a semi-arid region. This gives the delta great importance as a source of water, but raises the question – where does the water come from?

The answer lies in the Angola Highlands, 1,000 km to the northwest. Here, runoff from heavy rains during December and January, fills the headwater tributaries of the river Okavango. The floodwaters flow downstream until they spill into the delta in June (Figure G).

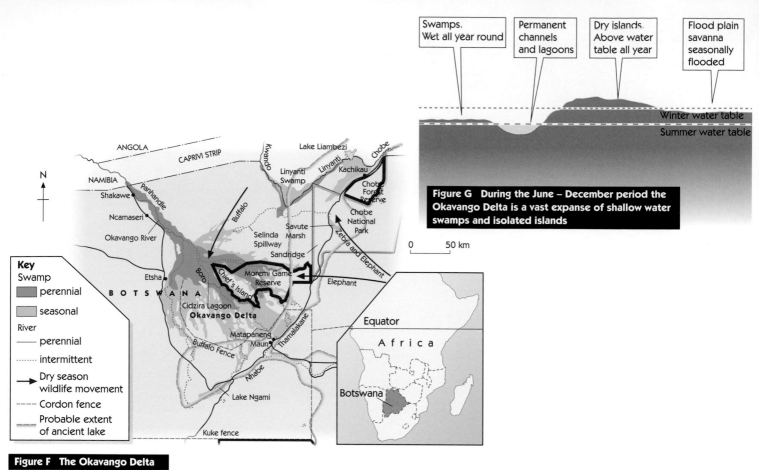

Swamps. Wet all year round

Permanent channels and lagoons

Dry islands. Above water table all year

Flood plain savanna seasonally flooded

Winter water table

Summer water table

Figure G   During the June – December period the Okavango Delta is a vast expanse of shallow water swamps and isolated islands

Figure F   The Okavango Delta

Figure H is an open system at work. The floods deliver an average of 350 billion cubic feet of water. As it emerges from the Panhandle floodplain, the water spreads in shallow sheets across the broad fan of the delta surface. Some seeps downwards and refills the groundwater store. Only 3% flows out of the delta. The remaining 97% enters the groundwater store or is lost by **evaporation** and **transpiration**. The floods also bring over 700,000 tonnes of nutrient-rich sediment and organic debris each year. This helps to make the delta very fertile.

The natural system at work

This tropical wetland is highly productive. It is a biodiverse ecosystem: a wide range of plants (producers) support many species of fish, animals and birds (herbivores and carnivores). Some of the wildlife live in the delta all year round. However, the delta is surrounded by savannah and semi-desert environments which have long dry seasons. The Okavango floods arrive in the middle of this dry season. As a result, vast numbers of birds and animals travel hundreds of kilometres to eat and drink in the delta wetlands (Figure F). When the rains bring water and vegetation growth back to the savannahs, the wildlife disperses once more. Therefore the delta is an open system.

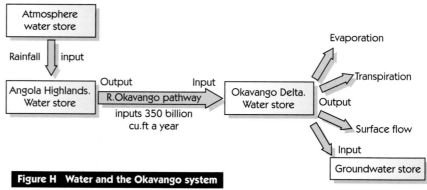

Figure H   Water and the Okavango system

▼ Questions

Look at the cross-section in Figure G.

5 In one sentence, describe the Okavango landscape during the flood season.

6 Give one important difference between the delta environment in the flood season and the low water season.

7 The delta has three types of environment: perennial swamp; seasonal swamp; land always above water level. How does this help to explain the great variety of plants and wildlife (biodiversity) found in the Okavango Delta?

8 The delta floods are at their peak from July to November. Give one reason why this timing is so important for birds and animals who live on the surrounding savannahs.

9 The delta is a huge store of water and food. Explain briefly:
   a   how water is an example of an INPUT to this store;
   b   how water and food become OUTPUTS from this store.

10 Complete the following sentence: 'The Okavango Delta is an open system because…'

Pressures produced by human activities

Human activities inside and outside the delta are putting increasing pressure upon the Okavango environment and affecting its sustainability (Figure I). These threats to the Okavango system are caused by three main forces:

- Drawing off of water from the Okavango river and delta.
- Population growth in Botswana causing increasing demands for land and water.
- Rapid growth of tourism.

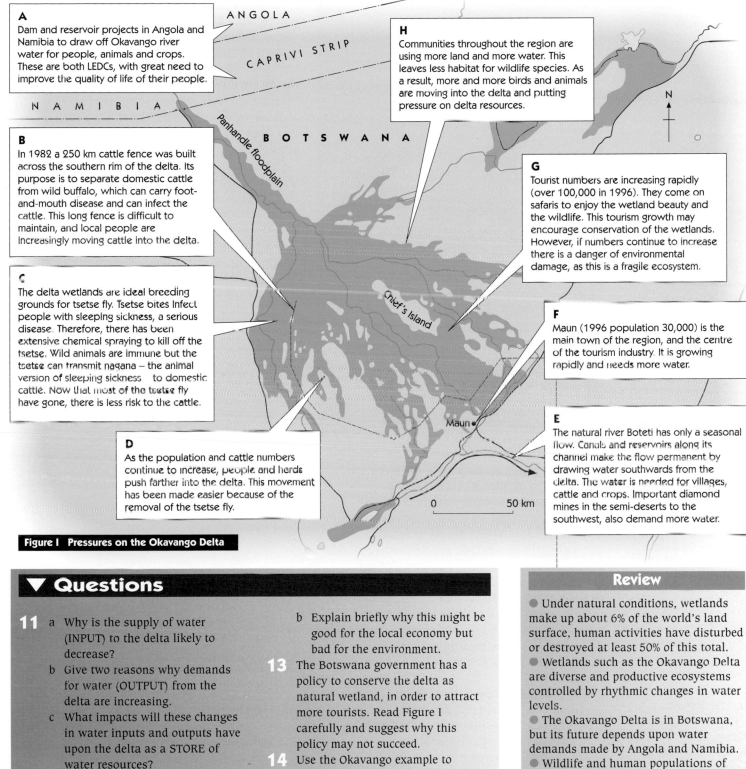

A Dam and reservoir projects in Angola and Namibia to draw off Okavango river water for people, animals and crops. These are both LEDCs, with great need to improve the quality of life of their people.

B In 1982 a 250 km cattle fence was built across the southern rim of the delta. Its purpose is to separate domestic cattle from wild buffalo, which can carry foot-and-mouth disease and can infect the cattle. This long fence is difficult to maintain, and local people are increasingly moving cattle into the delta.

C The delta wetlands are ideal breeding grounds for tsetse fly. Tsetse bites infect people with sleeping sickness, a serious disease. Therefore, there has been extensive chemical spraying to kill off the tsetse. Wild animals are immune but the tsetse can transmit nagana – the animal version of sleeping sickness – to domestic cattle. Now that most of the tsetse fly have gone, there is less risk to the cattle.

D As the population and cattle numbers continue to increase, people and herds push farther into the delta. This movement has been made easier because of the removal of the tsetse fly.

H Communities throughout the region are using more land and more water. This leaves less habitat for wildlife species. As a result, more and more birds and animals are moving into the delta and putting pressure on delta resources.

G Tourist numbers are increasing rapidly (over 100,000 in 1996). They come on safaris to enjoy the wetland beauty and the wildlife. This tourism growth may encourage conservation of the wetlands. However, if numbers continue to increase there is a danger of environmental damage, as this is a fragile ecosystem.

F Maun (1996 population 30,000) is the main town of the region, and the centre of the tourism industry. It is growing rapidly and needs more water.

E The natural river Boteti has only a seasonal flow. Canals and reservoirs along its channel make the flow permanent by drawing water southwards from the delta. The water is needed for villages, cattle and crops. Important diamond mines in the semi-deserts to the southwest, also demand more water.

ANGOLA
CAPRIVI STRIP
NAMIBIA
BOTSWANA
Panhandle floodplain
Chief's Island
Maun
0   50 km

Figure I   Pressures on the Okavango Delta

▼ Questions

11
a Why is the supply of water (INPUT) to the delta likely to decrease?
b Give two reasons why demands for water (OUTPUT) from the delta are increasing.
c What impacts will these changes in water inputs and outputs have upon the delta as a STORE of water resources?

12
a Give two reasons why cattle numbers in the delta are increasing.
b Explain briefly why this might be good for the local economy but bad for the environment.

13 The Botswana government has a policy to conserve the delta as natural wetland, in order to attract more tourists. Read Figure I carefully and suggest why this policy may not succeed.

14 Use the Okavango example to discuss this statement: 'The main threats to the sustainability of an ecosystem may come from external pressures'. ➡

Coral reefs

Reefs – beautiful, rich and fragile

Figure A The combination of corals and fish of all shapes, colours and sizes, makes a coral reef a place of great beauty. It is also a diverse and productive environment.

A coral reef is one of the world's most beautiful environments. It is also one of the most productive ecosystems. The biological productivity (how much plant and animal growth is produced each year) can equal that of tropical rainforests (Figure A). It is not surprising therefore, that people see a coral reef as an attractive resource. Nearly 9% of the world's commercial fish catch comes from on or near coral reefs. The tourism industry markets reefs as 'tropical paradises'. Reefs provide valuable building materials, e.g. reefs are the main source of raw materials for the tourist hotels on the Maldive Islands in the Indian Ocean.

The problem is that a coral reef is a fragile environment. The species that make up the reef ecosystem are specialised. That is, they need very particular living conditions and do not adapt easily to environmental changes, e.g. increased fishing, more tourists, severe storms, cooler water. The case study in this unit, Heron Island, Australia, helps you to understand this delicate balance in a coral reef.

What is a coral reef?

A coral is a plant-like animal. Individual coral polyps feed, and build up calcareous frames. A reef is built by the accumulation of the skeletal growth of millions of individual coral animals. Upward and outward growth can be as much as 20–40 cm a century. Corals are tropical marine creatures. They need sea water temperatures of at least 18°C; a water depth no more than 15 m and clear waters to allow the penetration of sunlight.

Another vital component is coralline algae (Figure B). These plant organisms form a hard surface skin over areas of dead coral. Colours range from pink through green to dark blue and brown. There is a close interaction between coral and algae. This is called a **symbiotic** (two-way) relationship. Without algae the coral may not flourish.

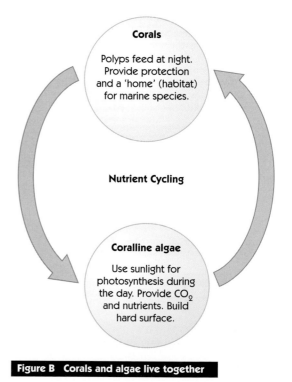

Corals

Polyps feed at night. Provide protection and a 'home' (habitat) for marine species.

Nutrient Cycling

Coralline algae

Use sunlight for photosynthesis during the day. Provide CO_2 and nutrients. Build hard surface.

Figure B Corals and algae live together

When we refer to a coral we mean more than the ridge of living coral and algae that surfaces at low tide. The majority of a reef is calcareous (calcium-rich) rock built of the remains of dead organisms.

A reef as an open system

Every reef is different. But we can group them into three main types, according to their location:

● **Fringing reefs**: Attached to or close to a landmass, e.g. around several of the British Virgin Islands.

● **Barrier reefs**: Offshore linear reefs in the shallow waters of a continental shelf, e.g. 1–50 km offshore from Belize, Central America; Australia's Great Barrier Reef.

● **Atolls**: Oceanic reefs in shallow seas completely detached from a landmass, e.g. the Maldives.

All reefs work as open systems. Figure C shows the interactions and interdependence between a barrier reef, coastal mangroves and open ocean environments.

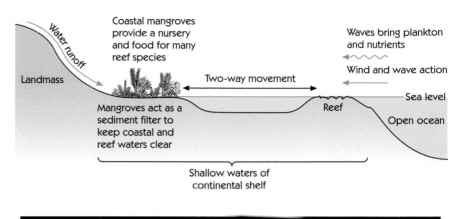

Figure C   A coral reef as an open system

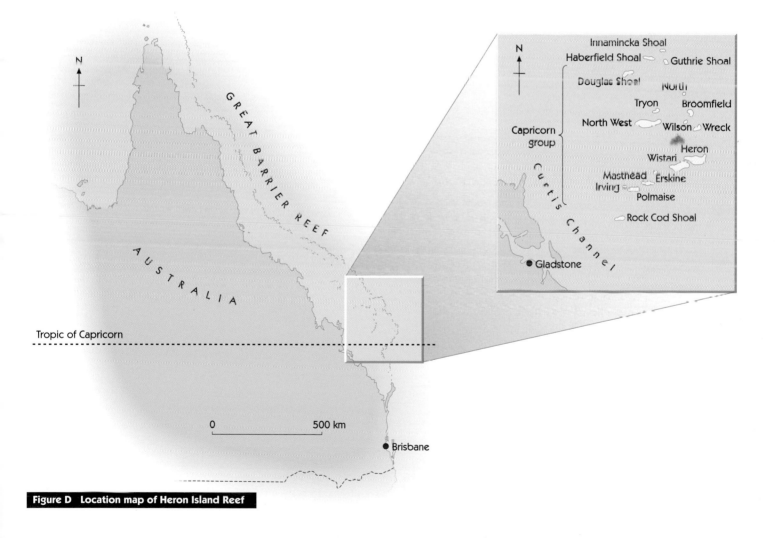

Figure D   Location map of Heron Island Reef

Heron Island is part of the Capricorn group, lying at the southern end of Australia's Great Barrier Reef (Figure D). It lies on the Tropic of Capricorn and water temperatures range from 27°C in summer (January) to 21°C in winter (July).

From the air it looks like a small island surrounded by a shallow lagoon. However, fieldwork shows that the reef is a complex environment (Figure E). Notice that the term 'reef' refers to the complete unit: the coral rim, lagoons and cay. The sandy cay (small island), at the western end of the lagoon, is built of coral fragments. The whole reef environment is delicately adjusted to water levels and depth. This adjustment allows us to divide the reef into a series of zones (Figure F).

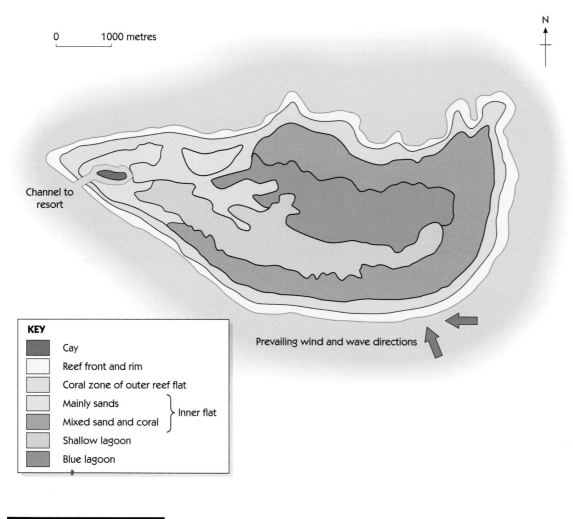

0   1000 metres

N

Channel to resort

KEY

▮	Cay
▯	Reef front and rim
▯	Coral zone of outer reef flat
▯	Mainly sands
▤	Mixed sand and coral
▯	Shallow lagoon
▮	Blue lagoon

Inner flat

Prevailing wind and wave directions

Figure E Plan of Heron Island

▼ Questions

1 Name two ways in which people use coral reefs.
2 Why is a coral reef described as a 'specialised ecosystem'?
3 State briefly the water conditions corals need.
4 What is the relationship between corals and algae?
5 Give one example supporting the idea that a coral reef is an open system.

Mean sea level

Reef slope | Seaward platform | Rock slope | Rubble crest | Outer or living coral zone | Inner or sandy zone | Beach | Sandy island | Shallow lagoon | Deeper lagoon

Reef front
● Sub-tidal (always below water).
● Main zone for vigorous coral growth.
● The platform is a coral terrace, 6–30 m wide, cut by waves in the shallow water.
● Corals grow profusely down the steep reef slope to depths of 15 m. This is where scuba divers see the spectacular diversity of reef life.

Reef rock rim
● Intertidal, and the highest part of the rim (except for the cay); 30–100 m wide.
● A few centimetres above the upper level of coral growth.
● Coralline algae produce cement to build a hard surface pavement.
● Breaking waves detach coral debris from the gentle rock slope (20–80 m wide) and throw them on to the rubble crest which has a cover of coarse debris.
● Seen from the air, this zone is located by a line of white breakers, as the outer rim of the reef.

Reef flat
● An extensive tidal pool, with a surface exposed at low tide; water depth at high tide up to 2 m.
● The outer zone consists of an uneven surface of living coral and algae encrusted dead coral; water depth, 50–75 cm at low tide.
● Corals grow to a maximum of 5 cm above low tide level, as they cannot tolerate long exposure.
● The inner zone is a broad expanse of coral sand with occasional clumps of living coral and algae crust. Tourists love this warm shallow water and sand for 'paddling', but the coral can be very sharp!

The cay
● A lens-shaped, sandy dome, built upon the reef flat.
● Composed of calcareous debris from reef organisms.
● 830 m long and up to 300 m wide.
● The windward southern slope is steep, with sand spread across a gentle lee slope to the north.
● Maximum height, 4.5 m.
● Beach rock zone up to 20 m wide.
● Gently sloping beach up to 30 m wide at low tide.
● Cay vegetation is adapted to survive in a salt-laden atmosphere and loose sandy soil.
● A central cluster of tall trees, surrounded by lower shrubs and then grasses, with herbs fringing the beach.

Shallow lagoon
● A broad sandy zone with few living corals. Currents and wave movements cloud the shallow water with sediment, creating unfavourable conditions for coral growth.
● Sand comes from the reef flat.
● Water depths at low tide are 0.3–1 m.
● Abundant small shellfish.

Blue lagoon
● Occupies the centre of the reef.
● 4.4 km long and up to 1.2 km wide.
● Average water depth of 3.5 m at low tide.
● A floor of fine sediment, an excellent habitat for small marine creatures.
● Water is clear enough for patches of living coral to survive.

Figure F The environments of Heron Island Reef

▼ Questions

Look at Figure E to calculate the following:

6 a The E–W length of the reef.
   b The maximum N–S width of the reef.

7 Construct cross-section A–B and label the zones

8 Use Figure E and your cross-section to write a brief description of Heron Island Reef (include size, shape and location of main features).

9 Heron Island cay is found near the western end of the reef. The cay is built of reef fragments eroded from the reef and transported by waves. Wave direction is controlled by the prevailing (most frequent) wind direction. In this case the prevailing wind is from the ESE. How does this understanding help to explain the location of the cay within the reef?

10 Select any two zones in Figure F. How does the work of waves and wind help to explain the character of each zone? (Think of the processes of erosion, transportation and deposition, e.g. where energy is high there will be erosion and transportation; where energy is low, there will be deposition.)

Human influences on the cay

The island is no longer a natural environment (Figure G).
● Tourism – A resort has grown steadily since the 1950s.
● Access – A channel has been cut across the reef to deepen the water to allow boats to bring the visitors.
● Research – Scientists have built a research station to study the ecology of the reef.
● Conservation – Since 1979 much of the island (and all of the rest of the reef) has been within the Great Barrier Reef Marine National Park.

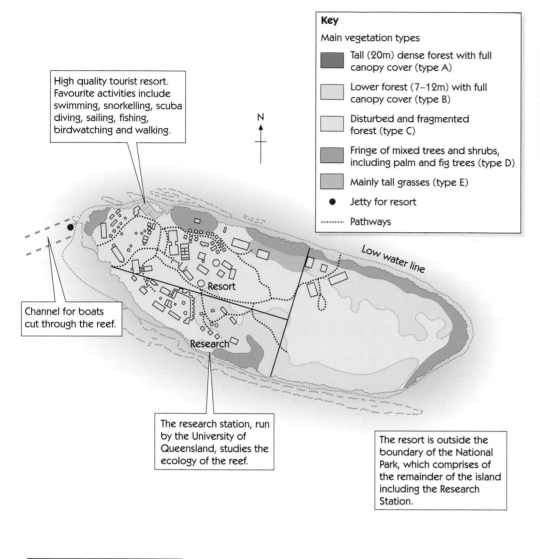

Key

Main vegetation types

Tall (20m) dense forest with full canopy cover (type A)

Lower forest (7–12m) with full canopy cover (type B)

Disturbed and fragmented forest (type C)

Fringe of mixed trees and shrubs, including palm and fig trees (type D)

Mainly tall grasses (type E)

● Jetty for resort

········· Pathways

N

High quality tourist resort. Favourite activities include swimming, snorkelling, scuba diving, sailing, fishing, birdwatching and walking.

Channel for boats cut through the reef.

Low water line

Resort

Research

The research station, run by the University of Queensland, studies the ecology of the reef.

The resort is outside the boundary of the National Park, which comprises of the remainder of the island including the Research Station.

Figure G   Heron Island today

▼ Question

11 Look at Figure G.
  a Approximately how much of the island is taken up by
     i) the resort and;
     ii) the research station?
  b The natural vegetation is canopy forest (types A and B) with a fringe of trees and shrubs (type D). Describe briefly the changes to this pattern caused by human activities.
  c Where is most of the original canopy forest found today, and why do you think it has survived in this location?
  d The resort owners want to expand the resort capacity. Suggest reasons why the scientists and the National Park managers oppose any further expansion. (Think of the island and the reef as a whole and what extra facilities a larger resort would need. Bigger boats would mean cutting a wider, deeper channel and would give a greater danger of damage and pollution. It would also result in more divers around the reef.)

Human influences on the reef

Scientists throughout the world are concerned about global warming. They believe that the greenhouse effect from increased gas emissions into the atmosphere, especially CO_2, is causing average temperatures to increase slowly. This will cause ice-sheets to shrink, releasing water, resulting in sea-level rises of at least 1 m over the next century. Environments such as coral reefs, which are delicately adjusted to sea-levels, are very much at risk.

▼ Question

12 Produce a labelled cross-section, suggesting what effects a 2 m rise in mean sea-level could have on Heron Island Reef.
  Hint – Draw a large outline of the cross-section of Figure F.

  a Add two lines: present mean sea-level; sea-level 2 metres higher. (Your upper line will be only approximate.)
  b Take each of the reef zones in turn and think carefully of the effect of deeper water, e.g. the power of the waves, currents and tides to erode, transport and deposit; the light conditions which corals need in order to survive.

Review

● Coral reefs are specialised, complex and productive environments.
● Living corals build up slowly on a foundation of dead coral.
● Heron Island Reef is a typical reef, consisting of a series of zones, each with its own character.
● The character of each reef zone depends upon its position in relation to sea-level and to the open sea.
● Coral reefs are very sensitive to human activities and to sea-level change.
● Coral reefs have both conservation and economic value, so policies need to try to balance both interests.

Mountain environments

Key ideas

● Change in one environment may have impacts upon other environments.
● There is a relationship between land use and environmental change.
● Sustainable agriculture requires a good understanding of how an environment works.

Main activity

Analysis of fieldwork data.

Do you know?

? Steep slopes and great altitudinal range are two important features which control how mountain environments work.
? The Himalayas, which form a huge arc to the north of the Indian subcontinent, are the world's highest mountain range.
? Despite the steep slopes and often severe climate, people have lived in mountain environments for many thousands of years.
? The Himalayas are the headwater catchments for the Indus, Ganges and Brahmaputra rivers.

CASE STUDY: The Likhu Khola basin, Nepal

The issue

The river Ganges is one of the great rivers of the world. Each summer, the monsoon rains of the Indian subcontinent cause flood discharges throughout this vast drainage basin. The floods move downstream until they reach the huge delta formed by the Ganges and Brahmaputra rivers (Figure A). The people of Bangladesh, who live in this delta, rely on the seasonal floods for their irrigated farming.

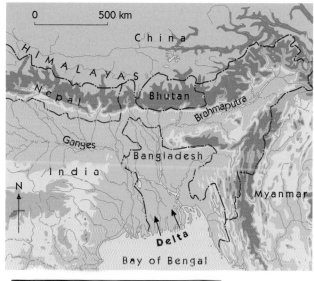

Figure A The Ganges–Brahamputra basin

However, in recent years there have been several extreme floods. Much of Bangladesh has been covered, with disastrous effects upon farmers' homes and crops. Some scientists believe that one cause of these violent floods is deforestation by farming communities along the southern slopes of the Himalayas. Most of the Ganges tributaries have their **headwater catchments** in these mountains. The scientists suggest that deforestation allows rainwater to run off the steep slopes more quickly into the streams. In turn, stream discharges build up rapidly, resulting in sudden flood surges along the main river channels. These floodwaters also carry away more sediment, which can cause problems downstream (Figure B).

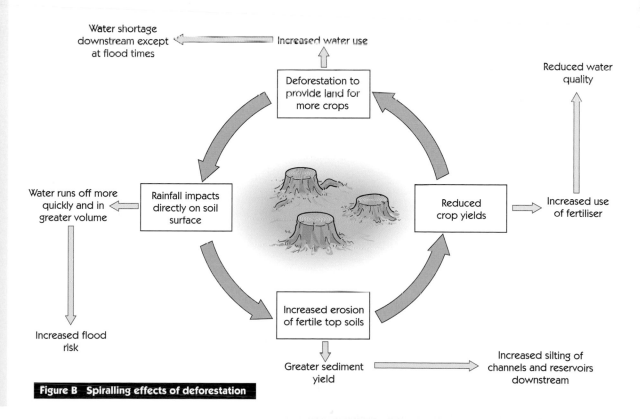

Figure B Spiralling effects of deforestation

Looking for answers

'An odd question came into my mind – can it be true that a Bangladeshi family in the Ganges delta may lose their home in a flood because a Nepalese farmer a thousand kilometres away works hard to grow more food?'

John Gerrard (University geographer)

John asked his question to several other scientists, and they decided to carry out fieldwork to try to find an answer. This decision raised some other questions, which we always need to think about before doing fieldwork (Figure C).

Where shall we do our fieldwork?

What sort of information do we need?

When shall we do our fieldwork?

How can we collect this information?

Do we have to get permission and co-operation, and from whom?

Has anyone else already done similar fieldwork?

How long will it take and how much will it cost?

Figure C

Selecting the study area

John explains: 'We chose the Likhu Khola river basin shown on the map (Figure D) because it has the features we needed. For example, a series of steep valleys cut by tributary streams, each with different land use patterns; extensive deforestation as farmers extend their farmland.'

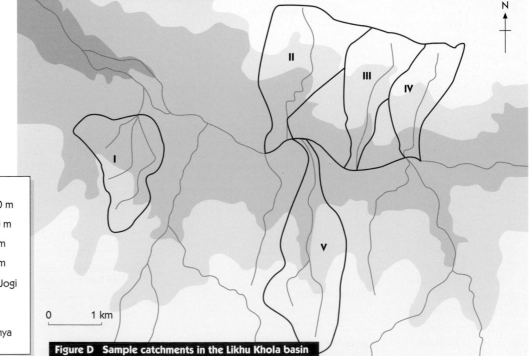

Key

	Over 1200 m
	900–1200 m
	600–900 m
	300–600 m

I	Bhandare/Jogi
II	Mahadev
III	Dee
IV	Khahare
V	Bore/Chinnya

0   1 km

Figure D   Sample catchments in the Likhu Khola basin

Organising the fieldwork

'Because we had limited time and money, we selected a sample of five small tributary catchments (see I–V in Figure D). Each has a different pattern of land use. For example, the Bore-Chinnya catchment (V) is still mainly forested, while most of the Dee catchment (III) is intensively farmed. We wanted to find out if the pattern of land use affected rainwater runoff and erosion. We then organised our fieldwork to test certain hypotheses. For example: Runoff and erosion increase as deforested area increases.

'We decided to carry out our fieldwork during the period of the summer monsoon rains. The mean annual rainfall in this area is 2,000–2,400 mm, and over 90% falls between April and September. Therefore, stream flows and stream energy are greatest during this period (Figure E).'

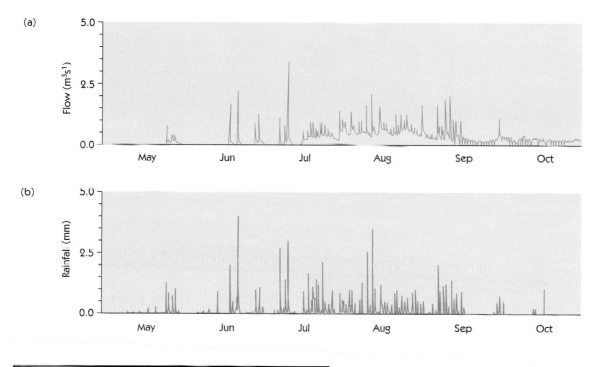

(a)
(b)

Figure E   Bore–Chinnya catchment: streamflow and rainfall, 1992

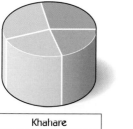

Khahare

Mahadev

Bore–Chinnya

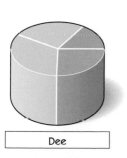

Dee

Bhandare–Jogi

Key

- Forest
- Grazing
- Khet } Terraces
- Bari }

Data collected

The fieldwork team collected data on the following variables:
- Rate and distribution of forest clearance.
- Changing patterns of land use.
- Streamflow regimes and sediment loads.
- Subsurface water levels and movement.
- Water quality.
- Types and distribution of surface erosion, e.g. slope failure; gullying.

Results of the research

The large amount of data collected needed careful analysis. The following is a summary of the results of this analysis.

Land use patterns

The researchers decided to group the land uses into three main classes (Figure F).

Figure F   Land use in the sample catchments

1 The forests are made up of remnants of the natural woodland which once covered the whole area, and recent plantations. The plantations are part of an ongoing reafforestation programme, mainly of quick-growing pines. The local people use the natural and plantation trees for food, fuel and building. Notice that only the Bore–Chinnya catchment (V) still has a forest cover of more than 50%. This is natural woodland.

2 The crop land is subdivided into two types of terraces. The bari terraces are found on the upper slopes and rely on natural rainfall (Figure G). The main crops are maize and millet. The

Figure H Khet terraces on lower slopes

Figure G Bari terraces on upper slopes

khet terraces have been built across the lower slopes (Figure H). They are irrigated for intensive rice growing.

3 The grassland is used for cattle grazing, and is found especially on more gently sloping land. The cattle are an important source of fertiliser.

A very diverse environment has been created by these human activities. The map of the Dee catchment (Figure I) is an excellent example of this diversity.

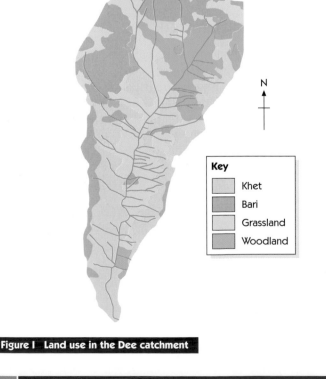

N

Key

Khet

Bari

Grassland

Woodland

Figure I Land use in the Dee catchment

▼ Questions

1 Describe the shape of the Dee river basin and the stream pattern in it.

2 Describe the location of:
   a   bari terraces;
   b   khet terraces;
   c   grassland.
   Suggest reasons for this distribution (use the text and Figures G and H to help you).

3 The whole of this basin was once forested. Give an estimate of the percentage of the area which is still under forest cover.

4 The largest area of forest is in the upper part of the basin. Suggest why this might help control runoff and erosion in the basin. ➡

Streamflow regimes and erosion

The graphs in Figure E give the daily rainfall totals and streamflow rates for the Bore–Chinnya catchment. Streamflow clearly responds both to the seasonality of the monsoon rains and to the individual rainstorms. Although most storms deliver less than 10 mm, severe events can last for six hours and may contain intense bursts of 2 mm per minute. Remember that the Bore–Chinnya catchment still has considerable forest cover. Therefore, surface runoff to the stream channels is slower than in catchments where forests have been largely cleared, e.g. the Dee catchment.

Soil erosion which delivers sediment load to the streams is caused by two main processes: rain-splash on less vegetated land and sheet wash from vegetated surfaces. Erosion rates vary widely according to land use, vegetation type and slope angle.

Soil losses from bari terraces are greatest in May after the land has been ploughed ready for maize planting. Over 50% of the total seasonal loss can occur at this time. There is further soil loss in mid-August at the time of the maize harvest and millet planting. Between May and August, erosion rates are lower because of ground cover by crops and weeds.

Land use	Surface cover (% of total area)	Soil loss (tonnes/hectare) monsoon season
Forest	95	0.1
Degraded forest	50	5.0
Grassland (Site 1)	90	0.1
Grassland (Site 2)	75	0.5
Bari terraces (upper slopes)	(a)	8.0
Bari terraces (lower slopes)	(a)	5.0
Khet terraces	(a)	0.2
Bare ground	5	18.0

Note: (a) No figures are given because surface vegetation cover varies through the planting – growing – harvest period.

Figure J   Soil loss by land use classes from sample sites, 1993

Figure K   Slope failure and gully erosion of khet terraces

▼ Questions

Use Figure E to answer the following:

5 Give the approximate date of the first measurable stream discharge.
6 During which month is mean stream discharge at its maximum?
7 During how many months does rainfall record a total greater than 1.5 mm?
8 During how many months is stream discharge greater than 1.0 cumec?
9 Describe the streamflow regime and its relationship to the rainfall pattern.

Look at Figure J.

10 Which types of land are at most risk from soil erosion?
11 Which types of land use conserve the soil most effectively?
12 Look again at Figures G and H. Suggest reasons why bari terraces are so much more likely to suffer soil erosion than the khet terraces.

Slope failure

The combination of steep slopes, heavy rains and clearing of vegetation can cause slope failures and rapid erosion (Figure K). Figure K shows that the slope has slumped. Water and sediment from this slump are destroying a section of khet terraces. Runoff and sediment supply to the main stream are being rapidly increased.

This research was co-ordinated by Drs. Rita Gardner and Alan Jenkins, and funded by the Overseas Development Agency (ODA).

The research conclusions

John Gerrard sums up their findings

'Between 1945 and 1960 there was extensive deforestation. This caused widespread erosion and gully formation. Since then not much woodland has been cleared. Indeed, the new plantations are increasing the forest area. As a result, fewer slope failures and gully systems have been occurring.

However, three recent trends do worry us. First, local people are increasingly cutting side branches from the trees. This breaks the canopy and allows more rain to fall directly on to the ground surface. Second, grassland is being converted to crop land. Again, this exposes the surface to direct raindrop impact. Third, as local populations grow and farmers try to increase their incomes, agriculture is being extended on to higher, steeper, marginal land.

The keys to conserving this mountainous environment are: keep bare surfaces to a minimum; control the movement of surface waters carefully. Figure L sets out our suggestions.'

Did John answer his original question?

John concludes, 'Well, the way the Likhu Khola farmers are using their environment today, they are probably not having much effect on flooding in Bangladesh. In fact, their reforestation programme is slowing down runoff and reducing sediment delivery to streams. Yet there are threats for the future if they go on extending their crop land and intensifying their methods in order to feed the growing population and to earn more money. Remember too, that we studied only one river basin. Hundreds of tributary basins feed the mighty Ganges, and each one has different environmental conditions.'

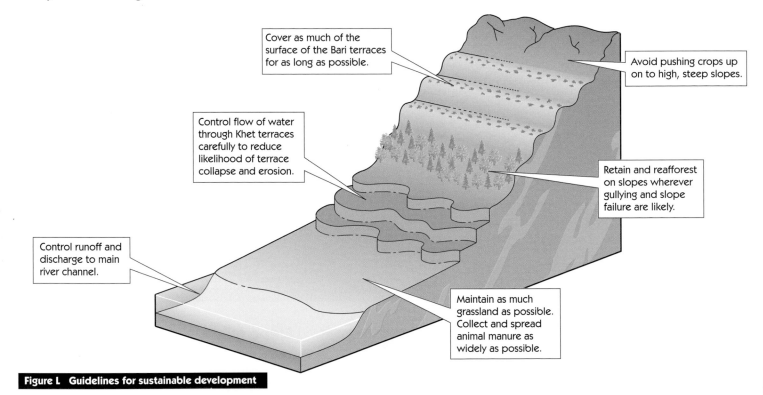

Cover as much of the surface of the Bari terraces for as long as possible.

Avoid pushing crops up on to high, steep slopes.

Control flow of water through Khet terraces carefully to reduce likelihood of terrace collapse and erosion.

Retain and reafforest on slopes wherever gullying and slope failure are likely.

Control runoff and discharge to main river channel.

Maintain as much grassland as possible. Collect and spread animal manure as widely as possible.

Figure L Guidelines for sustainable development

▼ Question

13 Outline the factors which influence erosion in the Likhu Khola basin, and give examples of the ways that human activities can degrade and conserve this environment. ➡

Review

● Headstreams of the river Ganges in the Himalayan mountains have strong seasonal regimes fed by snowmelt and monsoon rains.
● Deforestation of hillslopes in headstream catchments is one reason given for increased flooding in the Ganges delta.
● Research to test this claim requires the collection of data on important variables.
● Findings from one research project in Nepal do not support the idea that deforestation alone causes increased flooding.
● Erosion and rapid runoff are most severe where agriculture moves on to steep, marginal land.
● Reafforestation is a useful method for stabilising slopes, slowing runoff and sediment delivery to streams.

3 Water quality

Figure A The availability and use of water varies dramatically between rich and poor parts of the world

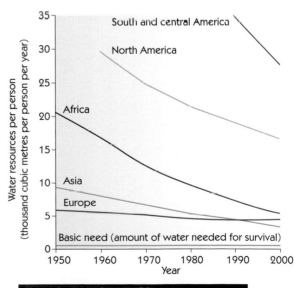

Key ideas & questions

● The provision of a regular supply of water has a major impact on people's health and activities. Water supply needs careful monitoring and management.
● What management attempts have been made to provide a reliable supply of fresh water in India?

Main activity

Presenting and interpreting data relating to the supply of fresh water on a global scale.

During the twentieth century, the number of deaths caused by unclean water supplies decreased dramatically in the MEDCs; fresh water is available at the turn of a tap. Elsewhere, in LEDCs, the situation is very different. While a family in Europe may use up to 3,000 litres of water each day, this figure is as low as 5–10 litres in parts of Africa and Asia. Without clean water, nearly one-fifth of the world's population have to rely on any water they can get. This water from rivers, ditches and wells is often contaminated and unfit to drink.

The greatest users of water are not the poorer nations, but rich industrialised countries. As economic wealth increases, so does the use of water for purposes other than farming (see Figure A). The economic growth of parts of Asia indicates that it is here that the greatest problems relating to water supply are likely to occur in the twenty-first century.

Do you know?

? Water is vital to human life, but most of our actual uses of water are not essential.
? Almost 98% of the world's water contains too much salt to be drunk, or be used in agriculture or industry.
? In LEDCs, 80% of diseases and a third of all deaths are caused by contaminated water.

	Total water used per person (cubic metres per year)	Agricultural water used per person (cubic metres per year)	Non-agricultural water used per person (cubic metres per year)
High-income countries	1167	455	712
Middle-income countries	453	313	140
Low-income countries	386	351	35

Figure B Water use is closely linked to economic development

Figure C Annual renewable water resources per person 1950–2000

CASE STUDY: Supplying India's water

India has the second largest population on earth, but only 4% of the world's fresh water supply. Access to clean drinking water and sanitation facilities is probably the greatest environmental and public health problem facing the country.

India's water resources are unevenly distributed, with floods and droughts being common throughout the country. Some drainage basins, like the Brahmaputra in eastern India have a surplus of water, while others face a severe water shortage. The main problem is that almost all of India's rainfall is received during the monsoon months from June to September. Runoff during these months is very high, and then there is a shortage of water during the dry months. The Indian government has built huge dams and long canals to help re-distribute the water, and dug wells to tap underground water.

The use of this ground water has increased dramatically. Ground water is readily available throughout the country, and is often cleaner than surface water. Increased usage, however, has resulted in the lowering of water tables everywhere. Water is being removed far more quickly than it is naturally being replaced.

The fall in the water table has been as much as four metres in the last ten years in some parts of India. Where this has happened, this has led to public health problems. In West Bengal, for example, water from deep underground is contaminated with arsenic (see Figure D). Industrial and urban waste have added to the problem. Where waste is managed, it is usually dumped above ground, with pollutants eventually finding their way into the local water.

An environmental health disaster is unfolding in West Bengal. Tens of millions of people in many districts are drinking ground water with arsenic concentrations far above safe levels. Thousands of people have already been diagnosed with poisoning symptoms.

Over the last two decades in Bengal, untreated ground water was heavily promoted as a safe and environmentally friendly alternative to untreated surface water. The origin of the arsenic is geological, being contained in the rocks underlying the surface.

Figure D   West Bengal faces health disaster

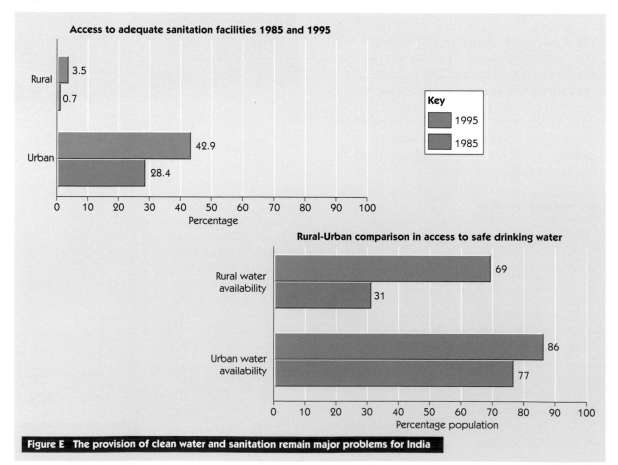

Access to adequate sanitation facilities 1985 and 1995

Rural: 3.5 (1995), 0.7 (1985)
Urban: 42.9 (1995), 28.4 (1985)

Key
1995
1985

Percentage

Rural-Urban comparison in access to safe drinking water

Rural water availability: 69, 31
Urban water availability: 86, 77

Percentage population

Figure E   The provision of clean water and sanitation remain major problems for India

Figure F Modern methods of obtaining water have created as well as solved problems

Water-borne diseases claim a large number of lives every year in India, despite improved health facilities and spending on health. Approximately 1.5 million pre-school children die every year from diarrhoea and cholera. Dysentery causes 60% of deaths in urban areas. River water in towns and cities is treated before being supplied to the public, but most rivers fall short of the standards set by the Indian government.

The situation is even worse in rural India, where the availability of fresh water has actually decreased in recent years (see Figure E). At the beginning of 1980, there were 230,000 water 'problem' villages in India, defined as being more than over 1.6 kilometres from a supply of clean water. Despite an effort to improve the situation, poor maintenance has resulted in many villages provided with wells returning to the 'problem' status after a few years.

The polluted nature of many of India's rivers has added to the problems. It was not until 1986 that the Indian government passed laws aimed at reducing river pollution. Even with legal backing, cleaning up India's rivers has proved to be a massive undertaking, as shown by the example of the river Ganges.

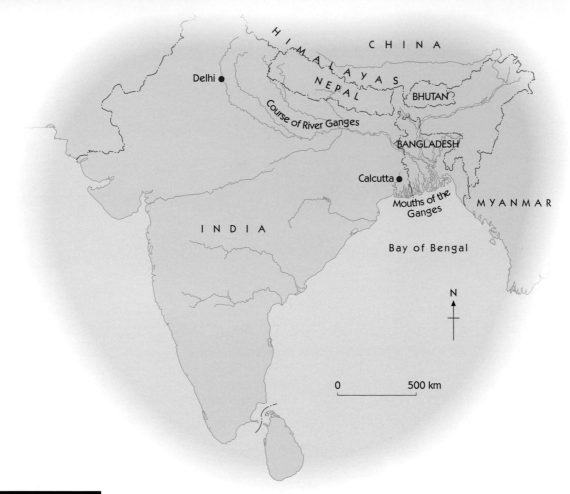

Figure G   The River Ganges

The supply of water in Delhi is not able to meet the current demand, which is higher than in other Indian cities. The situation is made worse by the number of diplomatic staff and tourists. The availability of drinking water is about 2,000 litres per person per day, whereas in slums it is less than 20.

The water supply is unevenly distributed throughout the city, with illegal squatter settlements as well as some new housing having limited access to safe drinking water. They use unsafe ground water for meeting their demands. Though the walled city of Delhi has basic infrastructures, 25% of the households do not have direct water supply connections.

Water shortage was considered the most serious of the infrastructure problems in Delhi. The Delhi government has attempted to increase the amount of water taken from the Yamuna river by constructing several major dams.

70% of Delhi's total population and all of the illegal settlements do not have access to sewerage. About 250 million litres of liquid waste is generated daily, of which only about one half receives any treatment.

About 53% of the total population live in slums, illegal and legalised squatter settlements. The lack of adequate sanitation and access to clean drinking water is a major contributor to disease. Outbreaks of cholera, such as that in 1988 which claimed the lives of 1,500 people, have become a common feature.

Figure H   Delhi's water crisis

The Ganges – the polluted holy river

The river Ganges rises in the Himalayas and flows eastwards through Bangladesh into the Bay of Bengal (see Figure G). During its 2,500 kilometre journey to the ocean, it provides water for eight of India's states and almost half of the country's irrigated land. The Ganges basin is home to over a third of the country's total population.

Although regarded as holy by Hindus, the Ganges has become one of India's most polluted rivers. There are nearly 700 towns and cities in the Ganges basin, with 100 of these being located along the river itself. These urban areas release vast quantities of sewage, solid and industrial waste into the river, contaminating the water supply of one of the world's most densely populated regions. The situation has been made worse by the long held belief of many that the Ganges has magical self-cleansing properties, and by the many funerals held on the banks of the river. Bodies are burnt on piles of firewood, but with the price of wood rising steeply, many bodies are only partly burned and then placed into the river.

Population growth in the Ganges basin is increasing the demands made upon the river's water. Agriculture remains the main consumer; India has the largest irrigation system in the world. Despite government investment in irrigation projects totalling $9 billion, the yield of crops grown in the area is low. Land and water management is poor, with farmers often wasting water because they pay very low irrigation charges. The use of underground water is an alternative, but it is expensive as farmers have to pay for the electricity to pump water from wells.

The demands made upon water from the Ganges are changing. The capital region around Delhi is the focus of increasing urbanisation. With the area also developing into an industrial belt to rival the Bombay–Pune region (India's largest), providing clean water is one of the major problems facing the city's planners (see Figure H). The Ganges is relatively clean until it passes Delhi, where 18 major drains empty waste into the river.

Attempts to clean up the Ganges have centred on the Ganges Action Plan, started by the late Indian Prime Minister, Rajiv Gandhi, in 1986. Despite some successes, almost half of the $270 million available for the project was spent on the main river with little effect. The remainder of the funds concentrated on tributaries such as the Yamuna, which flows past Delhi.

Few people believe that the Ganges is any cleaner because of the Action Plan. M C Mehta, a lawyer in India's Supreme Court, suggests why India's environmentalists have struggled to reduce river pollution:

'The people are helpless. There is no political will to clean up the environment. Politicians have close links to industrialists. Political parties are even funded by these industrialists. They all put pressure on the authorities to adopt a soft attitude towards the polluting industries, and to get away with it.'

Country	Resources
USA	14,000
China	2,470
Israel	370
Russia	15,000
Egypt	30
South Africa	1,400
Netherlands	700
UK	2,100
Saudi Arabia	160
India	2,200
Kuwait	0
World average	7,700

'Resources' are measured in the amount of cubic metres of water resources available per person within the country.

A country is regarded as 'water stressed' if the amount of water available is less than 2,000 cubic metres per person, and 'water scarce' if this figure falls below 1,000.

Figure I   Fresh water resources

Questions

Figure I shows the amount of water resources available in eleven countries. Use the information in the table to answer the following questions.

1 Rank the countries in order of available water resources.
2 Draw a bar chart to show your ranked figures.
3 Shade and label the countries that are:
   a   water stressed;
   b   water scarce.
4 Add a line to show the world average to your graph.
5 Choose a suitable method to show the information contained in the table on a world map.
6 Describe and explain the pattern shown on your map.
7 What do you think would be the effect on water resources of an increase in population in the United Kingdom? Give reasons for your answer.
8 What problems does India face in supplying its population with clean water?

Review

The provision of a regular supply of fresh water is essential for human health. The availability of clean water varies greatly throughout the world, with the people of Europe and North America being the greatest consumers.

Although India has the second largest population on earth, the country has only 4% of the world's fresh water. The situation is made worse by the seasonal and unreliable nature of much of India's rainfall. Management plans have met with limited success, and India faces acute shortages in the future as population continues to grow.

Environmental pollution – how green is Britain?

Key ideas & questions

● Gross National Product (GNP) is an indicator of wealth that gives a partial picture of economic prosperity.
● Economic growth can bring costly environmental problems.
● What environmental problems have been caused by economic expansion in the United Kingdom?

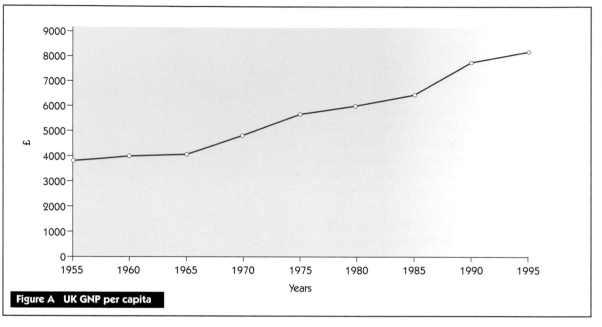

Figure A   UK GNP per capita

Do you know?

? The severe smogs in London in 1952 killed 4,000 people.
? Tall factory chimneys do not remove pollutants, but send them higher into the atmosphere. This results in pollution becoming dispersed, and often affecting areas far from where the pollution occurred.
? Carbon dioxide is a major contributor to global warming. The use of fossil fuels is increasing the amount of CO_2 in the atmosphere by 0.4% per year.

Since 1950, Gross National Product in the United Kingdom has grown steadily (see Figure A). GNP measures the wealth of a country's economy, and by the indicator of GNP per capita the UK is becoming more prosperous.

This progress is apparent in most European countries, but there is evidence that economic growth may be having an enormous environmental cost. GNP is the indicator most commonly used by planners and governments when measuring economic development. Although it gives an indication of prosperity, GNP takes no account of the drawbacks of economic growth: the loss of natural environments, traffic congestion, and especially the effects of pollution. Rising economic output may result in higher incomes, but does not necessarily mean a higher standard of living or better quality of life.

Pollution is costly to the economy of the UK, and could mean that current levels of growth are not sustainable in the future. As Figure B shows, it is air pollution from motor vehicles and factories which are the greatest problem. Although difficult to calculate actual figures, government estimates state that over 24,000 people are killed each year by air pollution in the UK. Environmental damage is a significant drain upon the nation's wealth (see Figure C). In 1996, it cost British industry over £6.25 billion in pollution control. Almost half this amount was spent on water protection, the remainder being divided equally between control of air pollution and the management of waste. The chemical and food industries have spent the most on pollution control. Despite the efforts of many local authorities, it is estimated that fewer than one in five households in the UK recycle domestic waste.

Emissions	Thousands of tonnes
Smoke	452
Carbon monoxide	5,328
Lead	2,761
Carbon dioxide	577
Methane	4,105
Nitrogen dioxide	2
Sulphur dioxide	3,264
Ammonia	320

Figure B   UK atmospheric emissions

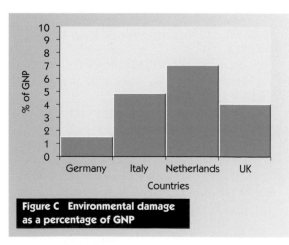

Figure C   Environmental damage as a percentage of GNP

The word **smog** suggests a combination of smoke and fog, and is generally associated with the atmospheric pollution which killed thousands of people in British towns and cities in the 1950s. In fact, smog is a more complicated mixture, and is a present day problem in rural as well as urban areas of the UK.

During winter, some weather conditions make it difficult for pollution to escape. On cold calm days, it is possible for pollution to be trapped near to ground level by a layer of cold air above urban areas (see Figure D). These conditions are common on frosty mornings following a cloudless night. Winter smog consists of smoke particles, sulphur dioxide and carbon monoxide, as well as traces of toxic substances such as benzene. The main source of these pollutants is motor vehicle exhausts, and the urban and domestic burning of fossil fuels.

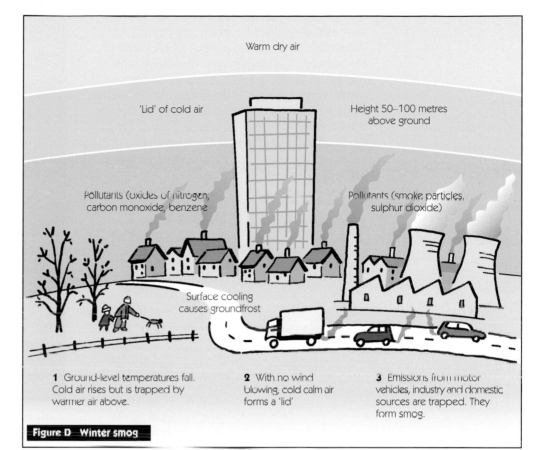

Warm dry air

'Lid' of cold air

Height 50–100 metres above ground

Pollutants (oxides of nitrogen, carbon monoxide, benzene

Pollutants (smoke particles, sulphur dioxide)

Surface cooling causes groundfrost

1 Ground-level temperatures fall. Cold air rises but is trapped by warmer air above.

2 With no wind blowing, cold calm air forms a 'lid'

3 Emissions from motor vehicles, industry and domestic sources are trapped. They form smog.

Figure D   Winter smog

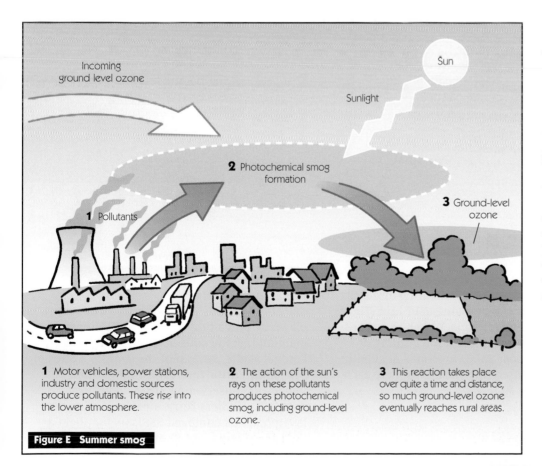

Incoming ground level ozone

Sun

Sunlight

2 Photochemical smog formation

3 Ground-level ozone

1 Pollutants

1 Motor vehicles, power stations, industry and domestic sources produce pollutants. These rise into the lower atmosphere.

2 The action of the sun's rays on these pollutants produces photochemical smog, including ground-level ozone.

3 This reaction takes place over quite a time and distance, so much ground-level ozone eventually reaches rural areas.

Figure E   Summer smog

Summer smog forms in hot, sunny weather. It results from the chemical reaction of gases with sunlight, and is also known as **photochemical** pollution. Motor vehicles are the main, but not only, source of pollutants (see Figure E). Smog levels gradually increase during daylight hours, becoming worst in late afternoon. It may take several hours for the chemical reactions to occur, and so the worst affected areas are often not where the original pollution occurs. Rural areas, downwind of towns and cities, often experience the most severe summer smogs.

Far from being a thing of the past, smogs still occur in Britain today. Although the Clean Air Act of 1956 and the move away from burning coal greatly reduced smogs, pollution is increasingly caused by traffic, domestic and industrial fumes. In November 1997, much of east London became covered in a thick brown blanket of cloud, a result of pollution from traffic and unusually mild temperatures. Figure F is a newspaper report on the scene at Canary Wharf in the London Docklands. Elsewhere in the world, city authorities have imposed measures to control traffic, the main cause of the pollution.

Figure G   Power stations make a significant contribution to air pollution

Return of the peasouper

The pencil-like point of Britain's highest building, the 800 ft Canary Wharf, pokes forlornly from a dense brown cloud.

Poisonous peasoupers have returned to London, putting at risk the health of thousands of children. Health experts believe that noxious clouds of traffic fumes, reminiscent of the choking smogs that killed thousands in the 1950s, could be to blame for the dramatic rise in asthma cases.

In parts of the East End and Docklands, where the smog is worst, asthma levels among children are twice the national average.

The smog has been made worse by the unseasonal mild spell.

Figure F   From the Daily Mail, November 1997

It is not only motor vehicles that cause air pollution. Power stations generating electricity emit sulphur dioxide, forming **acid rain** (Figure G). Drax, a power station in Yorkshire, causes the worst pollution, through the burning of fossil fuels. Almost 250,000 tonnes of sulphur dioxide are released into the atmosphere each year (see Figure H).

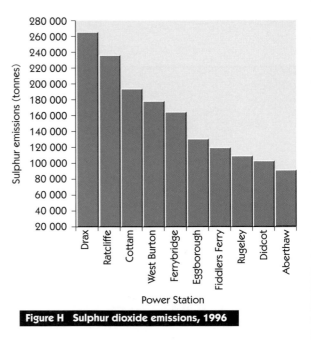

Figure H   Sulphur dioxide emissions, 1996

The effects of this pollution vary. While much is blown by prevailing winds to the European mainland, many soils across the UK have become acidic. Several of the country's Sites of Special Scientific Interest, Britain's most important conservation areas, have been damaged. Fiddlers Ferry, a power station near Liverpool, has damaged SSSIs as far afield as the Lake District and Snowdonia.

The good news:

1 Despite earlier predictions to the contrary, fossil fuels are not likely to run out in the near future.

2 The ozone layer. Production of CFCs, responsible for damaging the Earth's protective layer of high level ozone, has been banned in many countries and greatly reduced elsewhere.

3 Air and water pollution has been falling in MEDCs.

4 Sulphur dioxide pollution, one of the main causes of acid rain, has fallen by nearly half in Europe since 1980. During this time, the USA has reduced its sulphur pollution by one third.

5 Lead is disappearing from petrol, with leaded petrol being unavailable at petrol stations in Britain after 1999.

It could be worse?

The doom laden predictions for the British and global environment have forecast anything from the extinction of all sea life to nuclear catastrophe. To what extent has pollution been brought under control, or do we really face national and international disaster?

The bad news:

1 There may be plenty of fossil fuels left – so much, in fact, that they may permanently damage the world's climate.

2 Damage already done to the ozone layer is long term. It is likely to take over 100 years for the ozone layer to be completely healed, even if it is not damaged further.

3 Air pollution still claims lives: 24,000 each year in the UK alone, probably millions in developing countries.

4 Asthma, affecting one in seven children in Britain, is made worse by photochemical pollution.

5 Over two million people in LEDCs die each year from what is known as 'indoor air pollution'. This is caused by the burning of dung, crop waste and wood as fuel.

▼ Questions

1 Why is GNP per capita not always useful as a measure of wealth?
2 What are the main sources of air pollution?
3 Draw annotated diagrams to illustrate how smog forms in summer and winter.
4 Suggest ways in which it might be possible to reduce smogs.
5 Research the damage caused by air pollution in another country. Compile two case study cards, one for the UK and another for your chosen country. Your case study card should contain a summary of the main points you need to know on a card sized 20 cm by 13 cm (the size of a postcard). Case study cards are useful when revising any topic.
6 Read through the 'good' and 'bad' news about air pollution. Do you think it is right to suggest that the problem has been exaggerated by some people? Give reasons for your answer. ◆

Review

Although rising GNP per capita suggests economic progress, it does not take account of the environmental drawbacks of development. GNP per capita is rising steadily in the UK, but this growth may not be environmentally sustainable.

Air pollution, claiming 24,000 lives each year in Britain alone, is due mainly to fumes from traffic and factories. Smog affects both rural and urban areas. There is debate about the amount of damage caused by air pollution, which is often worst in LEDCs.

Traffic and the city

Key ideas & questions

● The increase in traffic in urban areas has led to traffic congestion and pollution in many cities, affecting quality of life.
● How have London and Paris attempted to solve the problems caused by increased traffic?

Main activity

A decision-making exercise relating to traffic management and planning in Paris.

The use of transport is growing rapidly throughout the world, particularly in the Asia–Pacific region. Although air transport is increasing at the fastest rate, road traffic is growing almost everywhere at rates higher than both population and GNP. There is a lot of discussion about public transport as it is more environmentally friendly, but the use of public transport is declining in many countries.

The increase in ownership, use and power of motor vehicles presents a challenge for cities everywhere. Traffic congestion in urban areas causes delays, air pollution and increased fuel consumption, as well as affecting road safety.

The management of road traffic in the early twenty-first century is vital for the sustainable development of the world's cities. Problems caused by the growth in road traffic outweigh any benefits brought about by improvements in fuel efficiency and pollution control.

Many city authorities rely on emergency responses to periods of severe pollution, rather than strategies to deal with the problem in the long term.

Figure A shows the measures taken by some of the major European cities. What are Europe's two largest cities, London and Paris, doing to solve their traffic problems?

Do you know?

? 25% of households in the United Kingdom own more than one car, compared with 10% in 1980.
? Car ownership in the UK is lower than in many other countries. 43% of people possess a car or van, compared with 50% in Germany, 53% in Italy and 59% in the United States.
? Air pollution recently became so bad in São Paulo, Brazil, that cars were only allowed to enter the city on a rota system.
? It is estimated that there could be as many as 40 million cars in the UK by 2020. Worldwide, the total number of motor vehicles is more than 600 million.

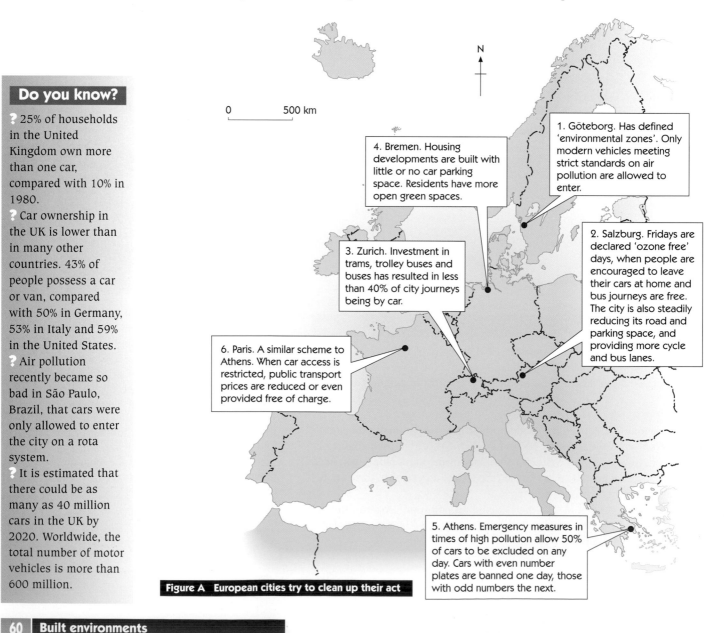

0   500 km

N

4. Bremen. Housing developments are built with little or no car parking space. Residents have more open green spaces.

1. Göteborg. Has defined 'environmental zones'. Only modern vehicles meeting strict standards on air pollution are allowed to enter.

2. Salzburg. Fridays are declared 'ozone free' days, when people are encouraged to leave their cars at home and bus journeys are free. The city is also steadily reducing its road and parking space, and providing more cycle and bus lanes.

3. Zurich. Investment in trams, trolley buses and buses has resulted in less than 40% of city journeys being by car.

6. Paris. A similar scheme to Athens. When car access is restricted, public transport prices are reduced or even provided free of charge.

5. Athens. Emergency measures in times of high pollution allow 50% of cars to be excluded on any day. Cars with even number plates are banned one day, those with odd numbers the next.

Figure A   European cities try to clean up their act

London

Like most other cities in the United Kingdom, road traffic is increasing, as is the range of reasons for these journeys. Although the majority of urban journeys are work related, 90% of shopping trips are by car. The use of private transport for leisure purposes has also steadily increased.

Some measures to deal with greater pollution and congestion have been introduced in British cities (see Figure B), although most have yet to reach the capital. With a predicted growth of 40% in London's traffic by 2016, several additional measures have been considered by the city authorities:

● Roadside pollution monitors could be installed, which would alert the authorities when levels of air pollution became high.
● Control systems could alter traffic light timings, in order to reduce the number of cars that could actually get into the city.
● Roads could be blocked, forcing motorists to be diverted to less crowded and polluted areas.
● Motorists could be charged to enter the city. Cars could be electronically tagged, so that charges could be made automatically. These charges could be increased as pollution became worse.
● Extra public transport could be provided in times of greatest pollution.

N   0   100 km

6. Edinburgh. 'City Car Club' provides 15 cars for the use of local residents. More than 15 miles of bus lanes, aiming to cut car use by one third by 2010. Pavement widening and road narrowing schemes, to discourage traffic.

2. Nottingham. Car sharing, car pooling and Park and Ride schemes aim to cut car commuting by one third by 2010.

1. York. The longest established traffic scheme in the country, with the central area of York being pedestrianised. Park and Ride schemes are estimated to have reduced private car journeys by 500 000 per year. Nearly a quarter of commuters cycle to work, and road accidents have been reduced by one third. 80 miles of pedestrian routeways are planned.

3. Leicester. A trial 'congestion charging scheme' where commuters have to pay up to £10 per day to drive in the city. The aim is to cut car commuting by 15%.

5. Southampton. University Hospital staff are banned from driving less than one mile to work, and are given a cycle allowance. Cycle route scheme to local schools aims to halve the number of pupils driven to school.

4. Heathrow airport. A bus lane to the airport, paid for out of car parking charges. Airport workers living in nearby Slough have free bus travel to and from work, others have special reductions.

Figure B   UK traffic reduction schemes

Figure C   London is one of Europe's most congested cities

Paris

In Paris, as in other European cities, the clampdown has already started. The city has a three-level system for coping with extreme pollution (see Figure D). At the lowest level, road speed limits are reduced and motorists are asked to leave their cars at home. If the second level of air pollution is reached, public transport costs are also halved.

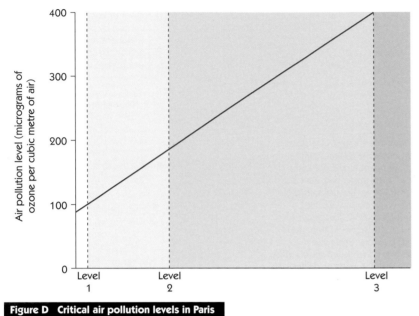

Figure D   Critical air pollution levels in Paris

The highest level of pollution results in car access to the city being limited, and all public transport being free of charge. At the end of September 1997, after a period of hot weather, Paris became shrouded in a blanket of smog. Pollution levels soared, and the highest level of air pollution was reached. The government immediately restricted the number of cars allowed into the city each day. On 1 October, only cars with odd numbers on their licence plates were allowed to enter central Paris. The next day, even numbers were allowed through, and others turned away (see Figure F). Motorists who broke the rules faced a fine of approximately £100. Commercial vehicles and cars carrying more than three people were not affected by the ban.

With the streets of Paris being unusually free of cars (see Figure E) pollution levels fell quickly. The French government sees such measures as only temporary. Longer term plans include greater investment in public transport, and in cleaner forms of fuel.

Figure E   Bus fares are as low as 24p when pollution control measures are enforced in Paris

Figure F   No through road on the Champs Elysées

Paris Transport 2000 project
300 Champs Elysées
Paris

Dear Student,

Welcome to the Human Resources Team of the Paris Transport 2000 project. As you will know, this is a major project funded by the European Union. The aim of the project is to recommend ways in which both public and private transport in the city may be managed at the start of the next century. We would welcome your views on this matter. You will already have some knowledge and understanding of the traffic issues facing Paris in the years ahead. In particular, the project team is concerned about pollution, congestion, and the need to control the growth of private transport.

In addition to background information, our researchers have provided the following:

1 Information under the heading, 'Traffic and the city'.

2 Various developments reported in the media (News reports – Transport 2000).

We hope that you enjoy your time with us, and look forward to receiving your contributions.

Yours sincerely

Marcel Blanc

Marcel Blanc
Project director, Transport 2000

Electric buses less polluting than diesel

Electric buses cause less pollution than diesel, even when the pollution caused by the power stations which generated the electricity to run the batteries is taken into account.

New Scientist

California abandons 'electric car' target

The American state of California planned to have 10% of its cars running on electricity by 2003. This target is not likely to be met, because battery technology has not advanced enough. This would make the cars too expensive to manufacture in large numbers.

Financial Times

Launch of French electric cars

France's major car manufacturers have all launched electric versions of their existing small petrol-based models. In what is expected to be a significant selling point, it is intended that the prices of the electric models will be broadly in line with their petrol-based equivalents. This has been possible because the manufacturers will receive 10,000 francs (about £1,000) for every electric car they produce, and every buyer will get 5,000 francs (about £500) from the French government.

The mobility of the French cars is limited because their batteries need to be recharged every 80–100 kilometres. There are around 120 public recharging facilities in Paris.

Le Monde

Greenpeace moves into car design

Greenpeace has invested nearly $2 million in developing a car which it claims can cut fuel consumption by half. The new efficient car is likely to cost up to 15% more than a petrol-based equivalent.

New Scientist

Mexico City curbs cars

The authorities in Mexico City, one of the world's most polluted cities, have proposed to ban cars for two days a week during smog emergencies. Cars are banned on the basis of the last digit of their number plates.

The Guardian

Figure H   News reports – Transport 2000

▼ Questions

For the purpose of this activity, you are to imagine that you are a student working abroad as part of your study. You are to join the Transport 2000 project team in Brussels, a group funded by the European Union.

You are provided with the following information:
  a   A letter of welcome (Figure G).
  b   Traffic and the city (pages 60–64).
  c   News reports – Transport 2000 (Figure H).
In addition, you should use your own research and knowledge of the issues involved.

Your task is to complete a report which includes the following:
1   What transport problems currently face Paris?
2   Outline suggested solutions to these problems.
3   What is your preferred solution? Give reasons for your choice.
4   Produce an information sheet suitable for distribution to the general public. This must be a maximum of one side of A4, and should inform people of the benefits of your chosen solution to the city's transport problems.

Review

Road transport is increasing throughout the world. The rate of this growth is variable, being greatest in the Asia–Pacific region. Cities are the focus of much road traffic, causing congestion and pollution. London and Paris are among the cities which have taken measures to control traffic, although many of these are short term answers. Longer term solutions include the improvement of public transport systems and the development of alternative fuels.

Urban environments

Key ideas & questions

● Urban growth is often linked to developments in transport and communication.
● Why has the town of Rugby in the English Midlands grown so quickly in recent years?
● What is quality of life and how can it be measured?
● How should a **personal enquiry** for GCSE be structured?

Main activity

Conducting a local enquiry based on field work, suitable for GCSE coursework.

Do you know?

? Although Rugby did not become a settlement of any importance until the nineteenth century, Roman remains suggest that the site has been occupied for 2,000 years.
? As well as the public school, the town is also famous for the founding of the game of Rugby football in 1823.
? Meriden, a village near to Rugby, is the geographical centre of England.

CASE STUDY: Rugby, Warwickshire

Rugby is a town in the West Midlands of England with a population of approximately 92,000 people (see Figure A). The growth of the town has been associated with transport and communications since the building of the railway in the 1830s. More recently, Rugby has become a hub of the national motorway network, a major factor in the rapid expansion of the town's population. Planning permission granted by the local council for industrial and residential developments has ensured that Rugby will continue to grow rapidly into the twenty-first century. What effect is such growth likely to have upon the local environment, and in particular upon the quality of life of its inhabitants?

The structure of the urban area of Rugby is shaped by several factors, as shown in Figure B. In the nineteenth century, the town was an important centre of the country's rail network. Although of lesser importance today with several disused lines, Rugby is still cut from west to east by the main London to Manchester rail line. The line runs to the north of the town centre, skirting the flood plain of the river Avon. Most nineteenth and early twentieth-century industry developed close to this rail link on cheap land near to the river.

Residential development took place near to the station and to the south of the town centre. By the middle of the twentieth century, most employment was to the north of the town, with most housing to the south.

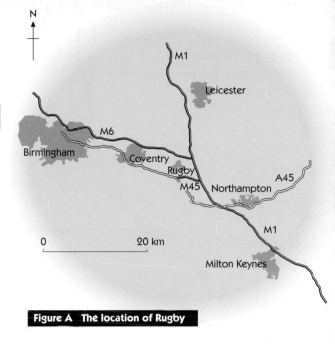

Figure A   The location of Rugby

Figure B   Factors affecting the growth of Rugby

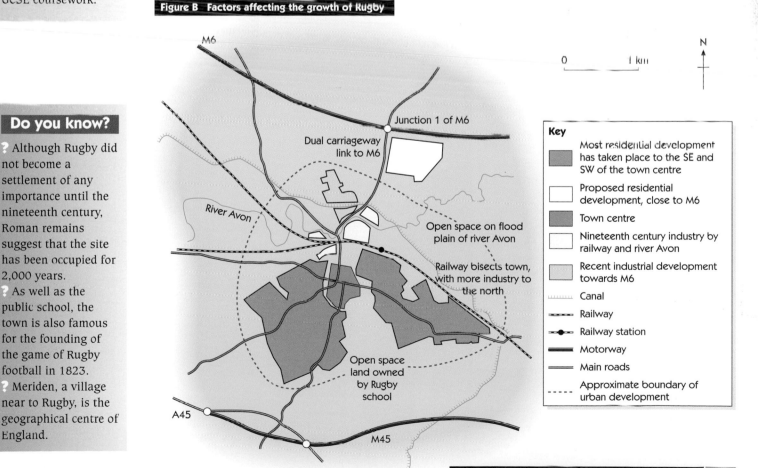

Key

Most residential development has taken place to the SE and SW of the town centre

Proposed residential development, close to M6

Town centre

Nineteenth century industry by railway and river Avon

Recent industrial development towards M6

.... Canal

Railway

Railway station

Motorway

Main roads

Approximate boundary of urban development

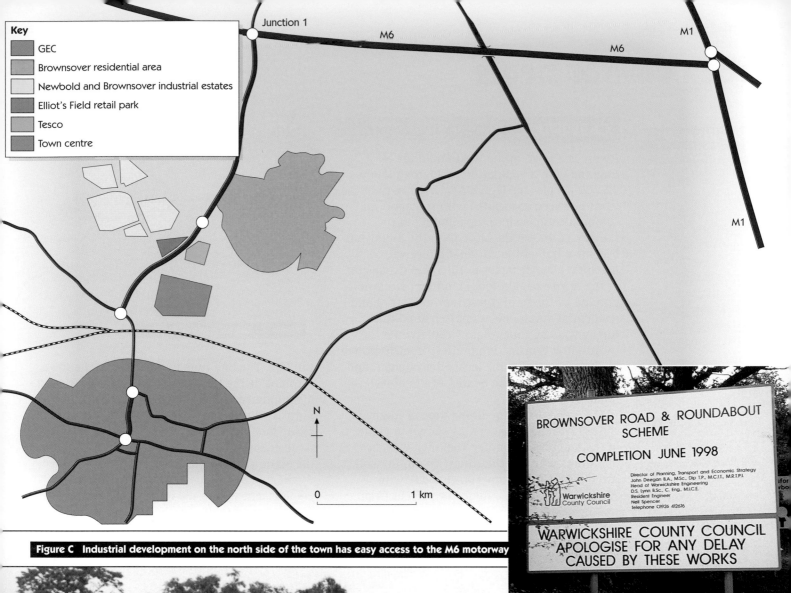

Key

- GEC
- Brownsover residential area
- Newbold and Brownsover industrial estates
- Elliot's Field retail park
- Tesco
- Town centre

Junction 1

M6

M6

M1

M1

N

0   1 km

Figure C   Industrial development on the north side of the town has easy access to the M6 motorway

BROWNSOVER ROAD & ROUNDABOUT
SCHEME

COMPLETION JUNE 1998

Director of Planning, Transport and Economic Strategy
John Deegan B.A., M.Sc., Dip T.P., M.C.I.T., M.R.T.P.I.
Head of Warwickshire Engineering
D.S. Lynn B.Sc., C. Eng., M.I.C.E.
Resident Engineer
Neil Spencer
Telephone 01926 412676

Warwickshire
County Council

WARWICKSHIRE COUNTY COUNCIL
APOLOGISE FOR ANY DELAY
CAUSED BY THESE WORKS

With the construction of the M6 motorway three kilometres north of the rail station, the town expanded in the direction of the new transport link. A corridor of residential, commercial and industrial land use grew alongside the dual carriageway road. Recent developments have seen industrial estates spreading along adjoining roads (see Figure C). It is likely that this continuing development will eventually see the town of Rugby reaching the motorway itself.

Throughout this time, the geography of the town has been influenced by one of its oldest institutions, Rugby public school. Located near the town centre, the school owns a sector of land to the south of the town which remains undeveloped.

Cawston Grange is a planned residential development on the south west edge of Rugby. A link road will take traffic from the new estate to the M6 to the north of the town, avoiding the town centre. The entire development is to be built on a green field site, mainly farm land. What has been done to safeguard the quality of life of residents on the new development and in adjacent housing?

Look carefully at Figure D, which shows a plan of the development. There are many environmental factors taken into consideration:

1 The development is to be built in phases. This is to minimise the impact of construction and associated transport for the local community. The entire estate is likely to take five years to complete.
2 A landscape buffer is to be placed at the edge of the area to screen it from nearby housing.
3 Existing bridleways are to be preserved.
4 Cycleways are to be constructed.
5 Existing features such as farm buildings and landscape features such as ponds are to be retained.
6 Approximately 20% of the area within the boundary of the estate is to be retained as open space.

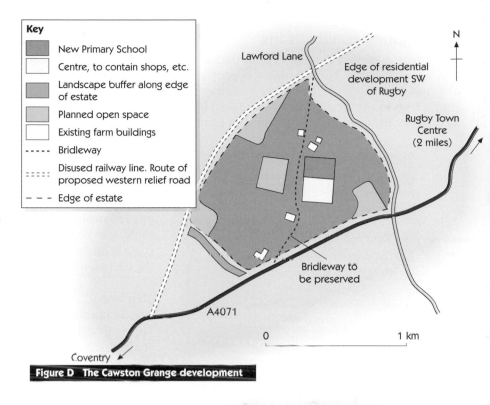

Key

▨	New Primary School
☐	Centre, to contain shops, etc.
▨	Landscape buffer along edge of estate
▨	Planned open space
☐	Existing farm buildings
-----	Bridleway
┄┄┄┄	Disused railway line. Route of proposed western relief road
– – –	Edge of estate

Lawford Lane
Edge of residential development SW of Rugby
Rugby Town Centre (2 miles)
Bridleway to be preserved
A4071
Coventry

0   1 km

Figure D   The Cawston Grange development

Figure E   The estate is a green field development on the south west edge of Rugby

Investigating quality of life

Developers may plan to reduce the impact of a new housing estate, but how do local people feel about such a change in their local environment? Figure F gives the viewpoints of some people affected by the construction of Cawston Grange.

a *We live on Lawford Lane, right next door to the new housing. It will ruin our view of the countryside; I think that housing development should take place within the area of the town, rather than making it bigger.*

b The real problem is the proposed relief road nearby, not the new housing. It will be within earshot, and will bring other pollution as well.

c I'm worried about people from the new estate using our road as a rat run to get to the main road to Coventry. The council should put speed bumps on the roads and make some roads one way, before there are any accidents.

d New houses, new shops, more jobs and prosperity for the town. Rugby is becoming a real growth centre for the Midlands.

Figure F   The opinions of some local residents

In order to establish the opinion of the community as a whole, it would be necessary to undertake surveys and questionnaires involving a large number of people. Although this is often not practical, a representative sample may be used. Together with personal observations, an environmental profile of an area may be constructed, the format of which could be used in other areas. This type of exercise is typical of the demands of many GCSE syllabuses, which require an enquiry based on field work as a piece of coursework.

Planning a local enquiry

In order to investigate a local issue such as quality of life in urban areas, you need to follow a series of stages, which are outlined below, and summarised in Figure G. Although Rugby is used as an example here, the same outline could be used to study any urban area. These steps could also be used to research many other geographical questions or problems, and form the basis for a study for GCSE coursework.

Step one
Decide upon a topic for study.
This will be decided as a result of your previous study, discussion with teachers, and through your own reading and research. The outcome of your investigation should be a piece of extended writing, and based upon a hypothesis. In the case of Rugby, a hypothesis could be, 'There are differences in quality of life in urban areas in Rugby', or 'The quality of life in Rugby improves away from the centre of the town'.

Step two
Write about your hypothesis in more detail.
What are the type of questions that you are likely to be investigating? Try to think of the factors which might affect the quality of life within the study area, and list a series of five or six questions. Two examples might be: a) what effect has construction of new industrial areas had upon quality of life in Rugby, and b) does quality of life improve with distance from the town centre?

Step three
Decide upon the data to be collected.
You need to decide what data are relevant to your investigation, and how it may be collected. Figure H gives some suggestions. Decide whether you need to use questionnaires, environmental surveys, etc. Always make sure that your data is needed in your investigation. Remember that, in this example, you need to find out about quality of life, and therefore it may be appropriate to speak to local residents. Design questionnaires carefully, and make them brief. Decide whether it is better to talk to people, or to post and collect completed questionnaires.

Choose your areas carefully, and remember that the time available to you is certain to be limited. It is not likely that you will be able to

Step one
Decide upon a topic for study.

Step two
Write about your hypothesis in more detail.

Step three
Decide upon the data to be collected.

Step four
Data collection.

Step five
Refine and present your data as maps, graphs, etc.

Step six
Interpret and explain your results.

Step seven
Conclusions.

Step eight
Evaluation.

Figure G   The stages in a personal enquiry or investigation

Bi-polar sheet

Date _____ Time _____
Location _____
Description of area _____
_____

Circle one number for each of the descriptions below:

Unemotional	1	2	3	4	5	6	7	Emotional
Ugly	1	2	3	4	5	6	7	Beautiful
Obvious	1	2	3	4	5	6	7	Mysterious
Harmonious	1	2	3	4	5	6	7	Discordant
Cold	1	2	3	4	5	6	7	Warm
Soft	1	2	3	4	5	6	7	Hard
Frustrating	1	2	3	4	5	6	7	Satisfying
Private	1	2	3	4	5	6	7	Public
Dislike	1	2	3	4	5	6	7	Like
Unstimulating	1	2	3	4	5	6	7	Stimulating
Full	1	2	3	4	5	6	7	Empty
Pleasant	1	2	3	4	5	6	7	Unpleasant
Disruptive	1	2	3	4	5	6	7	Peaceful
Disordered	1	2	3	4	5	6	7	Ordered

Street survey

Date _____ Time _____ Street _____
Most common type of house, e.g. Terraced _____
Approximate height of house in metres/storeys: _____
Age of houses _____ House price _____

	1	2	3	4	5	6	
The pavement	Full of holes						No holes
Parked cars	Many cars						No cars
Litter	Lot of litter						No litter
Grass verges	None						Wide grass verges
Trees	No trees						Lots of trees
Air	Lot of fumes						No fumes
Buildings	Run down						In good condition
Noise	Lot of noise						Not noisy
Street lights	Badly lit						Well lit
Other							
Total							

Figure H Data collection sheets used for a personal enquiry

visit all of your study area, so look for representative samples. If you decide to undertake traffic or pedestrian counts, decide carefully when to do them. You are likely to get very different results if you survey a main road or shopping centre at peak or quiet times.

Make sure that you have a plan for your data collection, so that you do not waste time. There is no need to analyse any of your data; this may be done later, and you need to allow sufficient time. If you decide to take photographs, ensure that you allow time for them to be developed and included in your completed work.

Step four
Data collection.
Ensure that you follow your plan for data collection, and that you are careful and accurate with the recording of your results.

Step five
Refine and present your data as maps, graphs, etc.
It is important that you do not simply copy out your results, but present them in the form of maps, diagrams, etc. Traffic counts, for example, could be shown by means of a flow line map, with the width of line being proportional to the amount of traffic. Questionnaire results could be shown by various graphs.

It is useful to include a copy of your survey results as an appendix, and to refer to these in your work. Also include any problems you encountered; any investigation is not likely to be completed without anything going wrong. You could, for example, have a poor response to your questionnaires. Bad weather could affect your survey results, even perhaps affecting your impression of an area.

Step six
Interpret and explain your results.
You should write at length, and consider each of the questions you introduced in Step two. Try to relate what you actually found out to what you expected.

Step seven
Conclusions.
This is where you should draw together your ideas. Try to write about general trends and patterns, relating your overall results to the original hypothesis. If appropriate, compare your results with any general model or theories; for example the concentric model of urban growth.

Step eight
Evaluation.
It is important that you include an evaluation of your investigation. In particular, ask yourself the following questions:
1 How successful do you think you have been in investigating your hypothesis?
2 How could your investigation, or part of it, be applied to other situations?
3 What would you do differently if you could repeat your investigation?
4 How could you extend your investigation if you had more time?

You should also include a bibliography if this is appropriate. Read through your completed work carefully to check for spelling, punctuation and grammar, and to ensure that your work has a clear and logical structure.

▼ Questions

1 Describe, using a sketch map, the factors which have influenced the growth and structure of the town of Rugby.
2 Why has the town grown so quickly in recent years?
3 Carry out an enquiry (or investigation) into the quality of life in a residential environment near to where you live. Use the outline given (Figure H) to help you. Complete similar investigations of other areas, and present your findings in the form of a personal enquiry.

Review

The town of Rugby grew in the nineteenth century with the building of the railway. More recent expansion is due to its location at the centre of the country's motorway network.

Rapid industrial and residential expansion has an effect upon the local environment, and the quality of life of people living there. It is possible to investigate quality of life by means of a personal enquiry through field work, which is an important element of GCSE syllabuses.

Changing urban environments – the West Midlands

Key ideas & questions

● The nature of urban areas is constantly changing. This is sometimes because of planned redevelopment, particularly in inner city areas.
● Decisions on change are often made by local authorities and national governments.
● What attempts have been made to regenerate the inner city areas of Birmingham?

FACTFILE

Population	5,400,000
Birmingham:	*1,030,000*
Population change 1991–2001	+ 2.1%
Population employed in services	68%
Population employed in manufacturing	26%
Households without central heating	23%
Housing tenure	
Private	75%
Local authority	21%
Housing Association	4%

The West Midlands — some socio-economic indicators (1997)

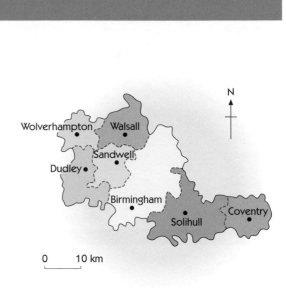

Figure A   The West Midlands

Main activity

Designing an advertisement to attract investment to Birmingham, and comprehension questions relating to the redevelopment of the inner city.

Until the 1970s, the economy of the West Midlands was dominated by manufacturing industries. In 1975 over half of the population of the region worked in secondary industries, notably car manufacturing. In the following decade, however, there was a rapid decline in employment in the sector. This was due in part to competition from abroad, increased automation, and also poor industrial relations leading to many strikes. Employment in Birmingham alone fell by 29% between 1971 and 1983.

The city and its surrounding region had to evolve from its long standing 'workshop of Britain' label. Birmingham City Council recognised the need to encourage other types of employment, and that the regeneration of inner city environments was vital for future prosperity. The success of the NEC, opened in 1976, suggested that there was scope to use Birmingham's central location and accessibility to develop the business and tourism industries.

Figure B   The NEC

Do you know?

? The National Indoor Arena hosts many major events. These have included the 1999 World Judo Championships, the 1998 Eurovision Song Contest, and the TV series 'The Gladiators'.
? The provision of efficient public transport is a priority for the local authority. Nearly 50% of Birmingham's households do not have access to a car, and half of the city's women do not have a driving licence.
? The West Midlands is home to over 900 overseas companies, and between 1994 and 1998 Birmingham attracted 20% of all inward investment into the UK.
? Birmingham attracts 42% of Britain's total conference trade.

Birmingham's Quarters – a plan for the future

Birmingham City Council's plan for the regeneration of the city is based upon **Quarters** around the central core of the city (see Figure C). Prior to any redevelopment, as much as 40% of some parts of the inner city were derelict. The city urgently needed new housing as well as employment.

Each Quarter has an overall plan, which is then divided into redevelopment areas. This hierarchy of planning is shown in Figure D. The Convention Centre Quarter, for example, occupies 200 hectares of land to the west of the city centre. The council's plan identified 12 key areas, with the Broad Street Redevelopment Area being central to the regeneration of the Quarter.

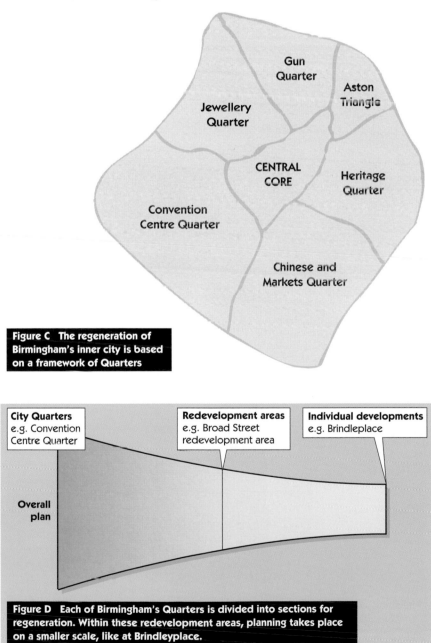

Figure C The regeneration of Birmingham's inner city is based on a framework of Quarters

City Quarters e.g. Convention Centre Quarter	Redevelopment areas e.g. Broad Street redevelopment area	Individual developments e.g. Brindleyplace

Overall plan

Figure D   Each of Birmingham's Quarters is divided into sections for regeneration. Within these redevelopment areas, planning takes place on a smaller scale, like at Brindleyplace.

The Broad Street Redevelopment Area

Broad Street is one of the busiest main roads into Birmingham city centre, linking it with the commercial offices at Five Ways to the west. In the 1970s the land along Broad Street was occupied by the remains of old manufacturing industries. Many buildings lay derelict, and over one-quarter of the land was vacant.

Figure E   Broad Street today

As part of the redevelopment of the Convention Centre Quarter, the plan for the Broad Street Area aimed to bring new and varied activity to this part of Birmingham. A major part of this scheme involved the construction of the International Convention Centre (ICC) and the National Indoor Arena. Both buildings, opened in 1991, were funded largely by the city council. The ICC cost £180 million, £50 million of which was provided by the European Union. The £50 million needed to build the NIA came from the UK Sports Council and private sector businesses as well as the city council.

Both developments lose money. It is the responsibility of the council to meet any deficit. They are seen as magnets attracting people into Birmingham, leading to the development of business and tourism in the city. The NIA has hosted major events such as the Eurovsion Song Contest and TV's 'Gladiators'. The ICC includes the Symphony Hall, venue for some of the world's greatest entertainers. In 1998, the meeting of the 'G8', the leaders of the world's eight most powerful nations, was held at the ICC.

Figure F Although neither building makes a profit, the NIA and ICC attract visitors to Birmingham. The ICC is the principal or 'signature' building for the Convention Centre Quarter.

Figure G Centenary Square, planned open space linking the ICC to Birmingham's city centre

The success of the NIA and ICC in attracting business to Birmingham led to other developments in the Broad Street Area. These include:

1 Centenary Square. This is a large open space linking the Convention Centre Quarter with the city centre. It also serves as a location for outdoor exhibitions and events.

2 The Hyatt and Novotel hotels. Built on land provided by the council, these provide over 300 bedrooms for visiting business people and tourists. The Hyatt hotel is linked directly to the ICC.

3 Renovation of the city's canal network. This has included cleaning schemes, canal walkways, and the promotion of boat trips and holidays.

4 Britain's first inland National Sea Life Centre, attracting family groups into an area of the city they might otherwise not visit. Over 500,000 people visit the Centre each year.

Figure H The 4 star Hyatt hotel was built on vacant and industrial land

Demolition and building work began in 1993. The area was to be 'people attracting', forming a link with the nearby city centre. Planning permission was granted for a variety of buildings, including entertainment, offices and housing. At the Water's Edge, for example, bars, shops and restaurants were built alongside the canal.

Figure I The renovation of Birmingham's canal network was funded by the City Council, British Waterways and the European Union

Figure J The Sea Life Centre

Figure K The Water's Edge and new construction at Brindleyplace

5 Brindleyplace, the final phase of the Broad Street redevelopment, representing an investment of £350 million by private industry. The development is an excellent example of how inner city areas have been regenerated jointly by the local authority and private businesses.

Brindleyplace occupies seven hectares of land to the west of Broad Street. In 1970, the area was dominated by nineteenth-century manufacturing industries, warehouses and derelict buildings. The success of the nearby ICC and NIA enabled the city council to obtain funding for the redevelopment of Brindleyplace from private industry.

When complete, the Brindleyplace redevelopment will employ 10,000 people. British Telecom, Lloyds Bank and Ionica have already established headquarters in the district. At Symphony Court 143 high quality apartments and town houses have been built, an attempt to encourage people to live near to the city centre. Comparison of the masterplan with the area in 1970 shows how completely the inner city area of Brindleyplace has been transformed (Figure M).

Figure L An artist's impression of completed Brindleyplace development

Figure M Brindleyplace before and after regeneration

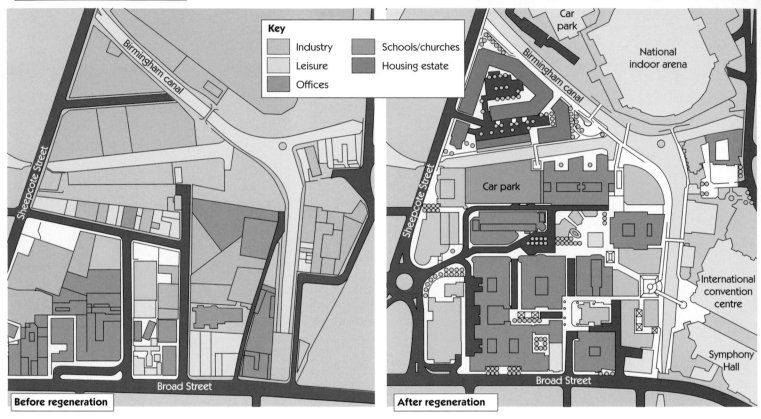

Key

	Industry		Schools/churches
	Leisure		Housing estate
	Offices		

Before regeneration

After regeneration

▼ Questions

1 What happened to employment in Birmingham in the 1970s? Why did this happen?

2 Why was the NEC so important to the regeneration of Birmingham?

3 How has the location of Birmingham made the city an important centre for conferences and trade exhibitions?

4 Why are the ICC and NIA both regarded as successful, even though they lose money?

5 Describe the main developments that have taken place in the Broad Street area.

6 Who do you think will have gained by the Brindleyplace development? Do you think any people will be against the scheme?

7 Imagine that you work for Brindleyplace plc, and are responsible for the sale of a new office block. Design an advertisement for a national newspaper to attract companies to locate in the area.

Review

Change is a continual process in urban areas. The process of change may be planned, and involve public and private initiatives. The regeneration of the inner city of Birmingham has been planned by the city council, based on a series of Quarters which are then divided into Redevelopment Areas.

Within the Convention Centre Quarter, the Broad Street Redevelopment Area has been transformed from declining manufacturing industry to an area attracting business people and tourists into Birmingham. The privately funded Brindleyplace development near Broad Street will eventually bring 10,000 jobs to the area.

Setting the scene

In Units 1–3 we have learned that:
- Environments of all types change.
- The demands people make on environments change.

However, change is only one of the factors to think about when we make decisions about an environment (see Figure A).

Change

What is acceptable today may not be acceptable to people in the future. Our values change.

Uncertainty

We have to make decisions without having complete knowledge about the environment.

Complexity

Many variables interact in an environment. So predicting how an environment will change is difficult.

Conflict

Different people and interest groups may hold opposing views about how an environment should be managed and used.

Figure A Factors in decision-making

As a result, managing any environment sustainably is complex. The case studies in this unit help you to understand this complexity. They show that sustainable environmental management is built around several key principles or ideas:

The example of the English Lake District, Figure B, (see the case study on pages 10–15) illustrates how they interact.

People
Farmers have created this landscape, but can – and should – farming continue in this upland environment?

Rights
Individuals and organisations own this environment, but does this give them the right to do what they like?

Scarcity
Can we satisfy the demands of farmers, foresters, visitors, environmentalists and people who have retired here?

Value
What is it about this environment that people value so highly, and how can we conserve this value?

Figure B Issues for environmental managers

The case studies in this unit use other high quality environments to introduce you to popular ways of putting the ideas into practice. These include:
- giving protected status;
- dividing an area into a set of zones;
- setting a **carrying capacity**;
- agreeing how much change will be allowed;
- planning for multiple use of an environment.

People	We have to manage the changing ways people interact with the environment.
Scarcity	We need to reduce conflicts which arise because of increasing competition for resources.
Rights	We have to balance the rights of ownership ('It's mine') with the responsibilities we have as stewards ('It's ours') of the environment.
Value	Environments have economic and conservation value. Policies need to balance these values.

Protecting precious places

Key ideas

● Environments with high conservation value need special protection.
● Dividing a Protected Area into a series of zones is a popular method used to achieve a sustainable balance between conservation and development.
● Each zone in a Protected Area may be managed with a different conservation–development relationship.

Do you know?

? Environmental value may be measured by qualities such as rarity, biodiversity and beauty.
? The Highlands of Scotland have been affected by a long history of human activity, but do contain the largest areas of semi-natural environments left in Britain.

Main activity

Map interpretation.

What is a Biosphere Reserve?

In 1971, UNESCO began its 'Man and the Biosphere' programme. **Biosphere** means 'living world', and the aim is to improve the relationships between people and their environment. One part of this worldwide programme is to give an area the status of Biosphere Reserve. The areas selected usually have protected area status in their own country, e.g. National Park, Nature Reserve. To qualify, an area must have at least one of the following qualities:
● Examples of plants and animals that evolve in a certain set of environmental conditions. This distinctive collection is called a climatic climax ecosystem or biome.
● Plants and animals (ecological communities) so rare that they are internationally important.
● Landuse systems that have helped make a landscape where there is a balance between people and their environment.
● High value ecosystems which have been damaged but are capable of being restored.

The United Nations is saying, 'Look, here is an environment which needs very special management'. In 1996, the United Kingdom had 11 Biosphere Reserves: 7 in Scotland, 3 in England and 1 in Wales.

How does a Biosphere Reserve work?

The aim of a Biosphere Reserve is to conserve a high quality, highly valued environment. However, it is managed so that people can use the reserve for several purposes. This is called a multiple use policy, and it works by dividing the Reserve into three main zones (Figure A). The core is the crucial zone where the best examples of the valued environment are found. The surrounding buffer and transition zones are managed to act as shields to protect the core. Biosphere Reserves vary widely in size, shape and character, but the three zones are usually present.

Core
● Contains the best environmental features for which the reserve has been set up.
● Protection and conservation are given the highest priority.
● Large enough for the valued ecosystem to be sustained over time.
● Access restricted to scientists and a very small number of visitors.
● Where possible, access by powered vehicles is banned.

Buffer
● Plays a key role in protecting the core.
● Human use must fit in with the conservation of the core zone.
● Some small-scale facilities for research, education and visitor use, with limited vehicle access.
● Local communities keep some of their rights to use the area in traditional ways.
● Apart from the traditional uses, activities focus on research, environmental education, and low density recreation and tourism that has little environmental impact.

Transition
● Managed as the link between the protected inner zones and the region around the reserve.
● Traditional sustainable uses encouraged.
● Small-scale settlements and low density road/track network.
● Experimental projects to restore damaged parts of the valued environment.

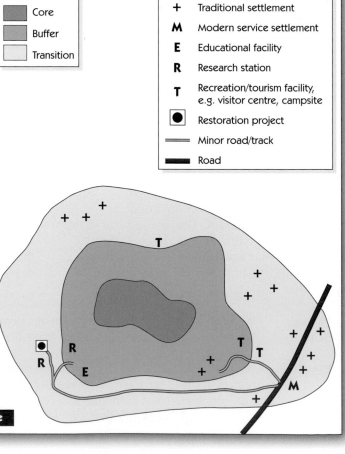

Zones
■ Core
■ Buffer
□ Transition

Key
+ Traditional settlement
M Modern service settlement
E Educational facility
R Research station
T Recreation/tourism facility, e.g. visitor centre, campsite
⊡ Restoration project
— Minor road/track
▬ Road

Figure A A general model of a Biosphere Reserve

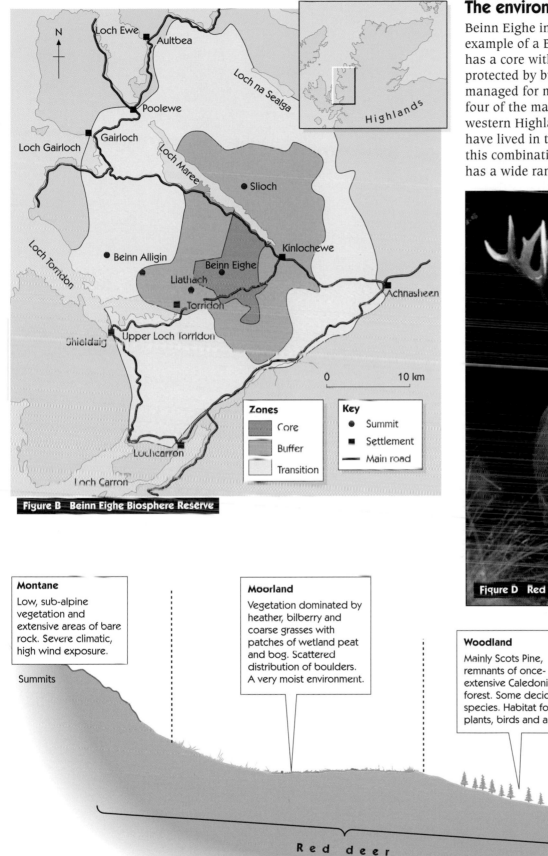

Figure B   Beinn Eighe Biosphere Reserve

The environment

Beinn Eighe in Wester Ross is an excellent example of a Biosphere Reserve (Figure B). It has a core with high conservation value, protected by buffer and transition zones, and is managed for multiple use. The core contains four of the main ecological communities of the western Highlands (Figure C). Because people have lived in the Highlands for many centuries, this combination is now rare. The Reserve also has a wide range of glacial landforms (Figure F).

Figure D   Red deer and habitat

Montane
Low, sub-alpine vegetation and extensive areas of bare rock. Severe climatic, high wind exposure.

Summits

Moorland
Vegetation dominated by heather, bilberry and coarse grasses with patches of wetland peat and bog. Scattered distribution of boulders. A very moist environment.

Woodland
Mainly Scots Pine, remnants of once-extensive Caledonian forest. Some deciduous species. Habitat for rare plants, birds and animals.

Loch
Aquatic ecosystem, adapted to cold water conditions. Rich in fish and plants. Pure water fed by rain and snowmelt.

Red deer

Lake

Figure C   Main ecological communities of Beinn Eighe

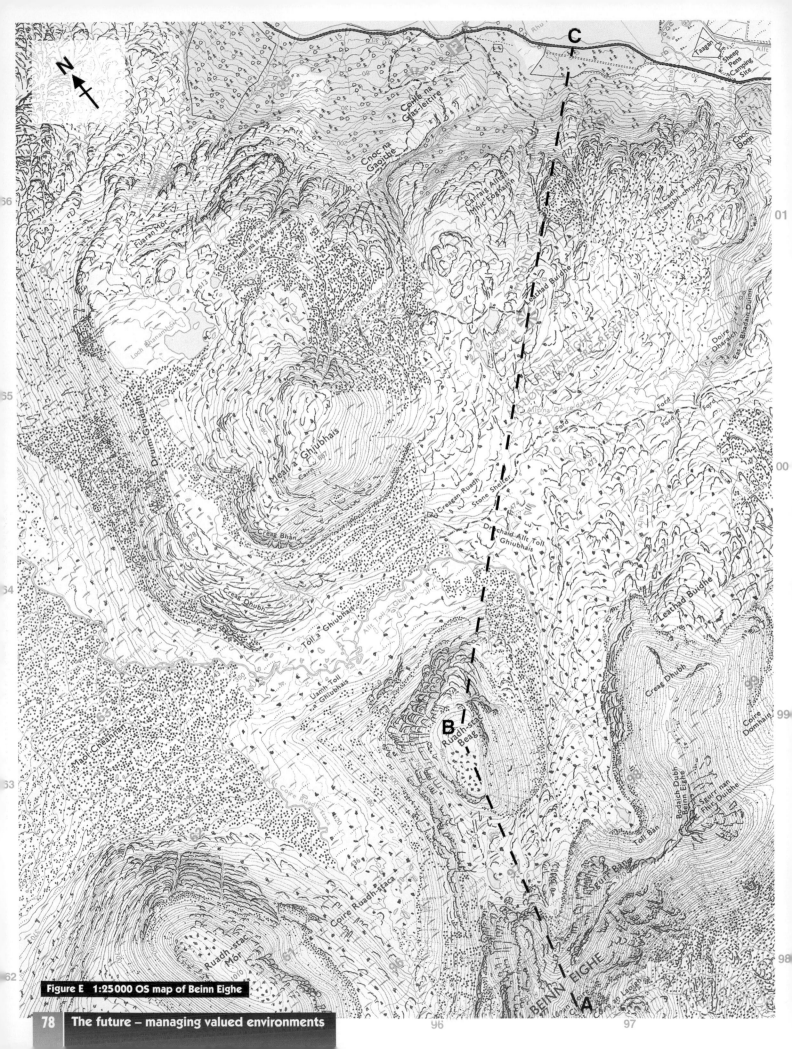

Figure E   1:25 000 OS map of Beinn Eighe

A31(T) or A35	Main road
P	Parking
X	Picnic site
☀	View point
- - - - - - - -	Path
▭	Water
⚬⚬⚬⚬	Scattered boulders
⚬⚬⚬⚬	Areas of loose boulders and stones
⌢⌢⌢⌢	Vertical rock face
⸒⸒⸒⸒	Moorland vegetation

Contours are at 10 metres vertical interval

Scale: 1:25 000

0   1

km

▼ Questions

1. Name and give the grid reference of the highest point on the map (Figure E).
2. Give the grid reference for the summit of Beinn Eighe.
3. How far is it in a straight line from Beinn Eighe to Ruadh-stac Mor?
4. Describe the distribution of woodland.
5. Name three features created by human activity.
6. What evidence is there that this area is used for outdoor recreation?
7. a Draw a cross-section along line A–B–C.
   b Draw a line below your cross-section and label it with the distance in kilometres.
   c Mark the boundaries of the four ecological zones – water; woodland; moorland; mountain. (Refer again to Figure C to help you.)
   d Above each of your zones, give a brief description of the landscape, e.g. relief, surface cover, drainage and human features.
   e Give two pieces of evidence that this area has been glaciated.
8. Key characteristics of the core zone of a Biosphere Reserve are diversity, remoteness (inaccessibility) and naturalness (how close to a natural condition). Write a letter to the Environment Minister supporting the designation of this area as a core zone. Give examples to support your case. ➡

Studying the environment

By reading a map we can learn as much about an area as we can from a book. The map key is its 'dictionary'. The map extract (Figure E) shows part of the core zone of the Beinn Eighe reserve. It is at a scale of 1:25 000, which allows us to study the environment in detail. The map is set at an unusual angle in order to fit on to the book page, but the North arrow will help you to orient yourself to the 'normal' map position. Most of the names are in Gaelic, the traditional language of the western Highland communities.

The map area extends northeast from the summit of Beinn Eighe (972 m) to the shores of Loch Maree, and so includes all four major ecological environments of the reserve. (Look again at the cross-section, Figure C.) As you become familiar with the symbols used, two characteristics should stand out: this is a wild, rugged landscape, and there are few signs of human activity. Remember however, that under natural conditions, there would be much more woodland.

Figure F The rugged, glaciated landscapes of Beinn Eighe

Review

● A map contains a great deal of information about an environment.
● Biosphere Reserves, designated by the United Nations are found in many countries and aim to protect high quality environments.
● A Biosphere Reserve has three zones: core, buffer and transition.
● The Beinn Eighe Biosphere Reserve contains excellent examples of Western Scotland ecosystems.
● The zoning system of Beinn Eighe Biosphere Reserve allows a multiple use policy which balances conservation with human needs.

Making conservation and enjoyment work

Key ideas

● National Parks contain landscapes that are highly valued.
● All human activities cause some environmental change.
● There are potential conflicts between conservation and development values in National Parks.
● Management policies attempt to reduce conflicts between conservation aims and the demands of various interest groups.

Do you know?

❓ National Parks are the most common class of protected areas, found in almost every country in the world.
❓ The United Kingdom has 11 National Parks, all in England and Wales.
❓ National Parks give protected status to many types of natural, and managed environments.
❓ In most countries, National Parks have two main aims: conservation and enjoyment. Trying to maintain a balance between these aims often causes problems.

Main activity

Using models to make generalisations.

Thinking about National Parks

The world's first National Park was Yellowstone, USA, designated in 1872. Today almost every country has National Parks. In England and Wales there are 11 (see pages 8–10, Unit 1). Governments pass laws that decide:
● what types of environment should be chosen;
● what the aims are;
● how the parks will be managed;
● how the parks will be funded.

For example, the 1949 National Parks and Access to the Countryside Act for England and Wales chooses the following type of environment:

'Those extensive tracts of country in England and Wales' which are to be protected because of 'a) their natural beauty, and b) the opportunities they afford for open-air recreation.'

Parks therefore, combine the twin aims of conservation and enjoyment.

When you examine a particular park you should ask these questions:
● What is the environment like? Is it mainly a built, managed, or natural environment? (Figure A)
● How big is it? For example, Yellowstone is bigger than all 11 UK parks combined.
● Who owns it? In many countries, for example USA, the government owns the parks; in the UK more than 70% of the total park area is privately owned. As you will see in the case study on pages 92–95, the aboriginal peoples own Kakadu National Park in northern Australia.
● Do people live there? Parks range from landscapes settled and created by people over centuries, e.g. UK and many European parks, to nearly natural environments, e.g. the Great Barrier Reef, Australia.
● What are the aims of the park? For example, in Australian and New Zealand parks, conservation is dominant; in North American parks there is a conservation–recreation balance; in the UK multiple use is dominant.
● Who makes the decisions? In North America, park managers have strong control; in the UK park managers say what they prefer, but must make their case through planning committees; in many countries, local communities are becoming more involved.

Figure A   The older building is the visitor centre for the Boston Historic National Park USA. This conserves the history of central Boston.

Figure C   Canyonlands National Park. Weathering of the sandstone strata has produced spectacular landforms.

The USA and Canada have some of the oldest and most famous National Parks in the world. For example, you can visit parks such as Banff-Jasper in Canada, or Yosemite and Grand Canyon in USA on mass package tours (Figure B). This popularity is not surprising, as they include some of the world's most spectacular landscapes (Figure C). They are also admired for the way they are managed.

'Loved to death?'

North American parks have two main aims: to conserve valued environments and to provide opportunities for people to enjoy these environments. Fortunately, almost all of the park resources are publicly owned, that is, owned by the government. This means that the park managers, who work for the government, have strong control over decision-making (Figure D). For example, they can use laws which ban commercial developments such as mining and forestry, big resorts, and hunting within the parks.

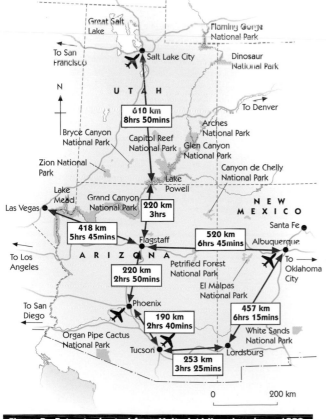

Figure B   Extract adapted from United Airlines brochure, 1998

▼ Questions

1 You are planning a fly-drive holiday starting at Salt Lake City and ending at Las Vegas (Figure B).
   a   How many National Parks could you visit?
   b   Approximately how far would you expect to drive if you visited all of them?

2 Give two reasons why North American National Parks are so popular.

3 Suggest three differences between National Parks in North America and those in the United Kingdom.

PETRIFIED FOREST NATIONAL PARK

UNITED STATES DEPARTMENT OF THE INTERIOR
NATIONAL PARK SERVICE

NATIONAL PARK SERVICE

Department of the Interior

a

Figure D A National Park at work

b

The decision-making chain

a

● This park is in the State of Arizona, but the land is owned by the US government.
● Department of the Interior (DOI) is the government body.
● The National Park Service (NPS) is an agency of the DOI.
● The park Superintendent and the staff make decisions and manage the park.

c

b

Today this is a semi-desert region. Around 225 million years ago the climate was wetter and forests grew. Fallen trees were carried by floods and deposited across a floodplain.
  Gradually they were covered by sediments. Over time, groundwater containing silica seeped into the buried logs. The silica slowly crystallised as quartz, creating what we call petrified wood. Erosion of the sedimentary beds is exposing the logs once more. Because it is rare and beautiful, people like to collect specimens – they are stealing!

d

c

This type of commercial development is avoided...

d

So that we can enjoy this.

A word from the Park Superintendent:

Responsibility ▶ Conservation ▶ Interpretation ▶ Education ▶ Understanding ▶ Enjoyment

'Welcome to the park. Our two main tasks are to conserve this wonderful place and to provide opportunities for you to enjoy the experience. But the conservation won't work if you don't help us. This is why we tell you about the park [interpretation]. We believe that as you learn about what you are seeing [education and understanding] you will have a better experience [enjoyment] and will respect the environment [responsibility] because you understand it. Have a nice day!'

▼ Questions

The photographs in Figure D have been taken by a visitor. The information is from brochures produced for visitors by the Park Ranger Service.

4 What environmental resources are being protected?

5 Give two reasons why this environment has been designated as a National Park. (Think of the purposes of National Parks.)

6 Describe the development in photograph C (Figure D) which lies just outside the park. Suggest why the park managers try to prevent such developments inside the park, and why businesses are keen to set up within the park.

7 What facilities and activities do the park managers provide and encourage inside the park? Suggest the type of environmental impacts these might have.

8 What policy does the park use to protect the petrified wood? Suggest one other way they could try to do this.

Look – snap – and go

Joe and Suzi Felice have three children, 6, 8 and 10 years old.

'The parks are great, but with the kids and all their stuff, we need our car. We like to drive around, stop at some viewpoints, take a few photos. Then we need to hit the cafés, shops and restrooms (toilets). The kids enjoy the displays in the Visitor Centres – they learn a lot about a park there. At night we like our comforts, so stay in motels and lodges. There are more vehicles all over the place these days, but the parks are big places, you know.'

Getting away from it all

Nancy McDaniel is unmarried and a member of an outdoor activities club.

'What we want to do is enjoy the peace and beauty of the parks. So, a small group of us drive to a park then leave our vehicles and backpack to remote spots. We haul in all our food and equipment, and may use campsites but prefer to 'free camp'. In some parks it is getting more difficult to find peace and quiet. People now have their noisy ATVs – All Terrain Vehicles – and snowmobiles and get into some real remote places.'

Action with ease

Tish and Dave Wilson have two teenage boys.

'We all love the outdoors, but tent camping is too much hassle. So we've bought a mobile home (camper van). We book into campsites which will take our type of vehicle – it's 34 ft long! You have to book months ahead, as it gets real busy during the summer. We take some tough hikes along trails, and in the evening we're sure ready for hot showers! We bring along most of our provisions but it's good to have a store (shop) after a few days. We also need gas and water for the van.'

Time to reflect

Marty and Barbara Carlsen are retired and are keen wildlife watchers and artists.

'We used to camp but these days we rent cabins away from the crowds. Luckily we can now avoid the peak season. Most days we drive to a parking place which looks like it doesn't have too many people. We take short walks then settle down to watch the birds and animals and do some sketching. In the evenings we often cook in the cabin, but it's nice to eat out sometimes. We also enjoy the talks the Rangers give at the campgrounds or near the Visitor Centres in the evenings.'

Figure E   Parks, people and points of view

The demand side – visitor needs and impacts

Managers face two central problems: visitors are increasing in numbers and in the variety of ways they want to use the park environments (Figure E). Each type of visitor prefers a particular type of environmental setting, e.g. being alone or with lots of people; a certain level of facilities, e.g. outdoor challenge or indoor comfort; and makes certain impacts, e.g. localised or scattered.

The supply side – management response

As they try to balance conservation and recreation, managers have two options:

● **Concentration** – Restrict recreational use to certain areas in order to protect the rest of the park.
Result: Concentrated use = localised intense impact.

● **Dispersion** – Spread the recreational use relatively evenly throughout the park, to prevent severe localised impacts.
Result: Dispersed use = dispersed moderate impact.

This seems a straightforward choice. However, park managers know that different types of visitor need different environmental settings. Look again at the four accounts (Figure E). For example, how would a concentration approach affect Nancy McDaniel? If the park managers adopted a dispersion approach, what would they have to provide to satisfy Joe and Suzi Felice?

▼ Questions

Read the four opinions in Figure E carefully.

9   For each visitor type, make lists of the following:
   a   the resources and facilities they need;
   b   the things they like to do;
   c   how they use the environment;
   d   the impacts they make on the environment.

10   Think again of the main purposes of National Parks. Which of the visitor types fit most easily with park aims and which are likely to create the most problems for park managers? Explain your choice. ➡

11   Which of the four visitor types are likely to get along, and which are likely to be opposed to each other – or would they all get along?

12   For each of the four visitor types in Figure E, state which of the two options (concentration or dispersion) you think they would prefer and give reasons for your choice.

13   Make two ranking lists for the four visitor types:
   a   according to the amount of change to the natural environment their needs require;
   b   according to the ease with which their needs fit with the conservation aims of the park managers.

As a result, many parks have introduced plans which combine the concentration and dispersion approaches. Yellowstone (Figure F) is an excellent example. The park is divided into two major zones, a frontcountry or development zone, and a backcountry or wilderness zone. In this and most parks, the backcountry zone takes up at least 90% of the total area.

A zoning model for National Parks

The general model in Figure H shows how the zoning approach works. The frontcountry zone concentrates visitors. The backcountry zone disperses visitors.

Frontcountry zone

In Figure G a road winds through or close to attractive features and sites. In some parks, cars are banned. You take shuttle buses and can get on and off as you wish. Where cars are allowed, there are car parks at the interpreted sites and where footpaths begin. Marked trails guide you on walks away from the road.

Key

- ·—·—· Park boundary
- ▬▬ Road
- ▨ Major lake
- ▨ Backcountry or natural zone
- ▢ Frontcountry or development zone

0   20 km

Figure F   Zoning plan for Yellowstone National Park

Figure G The frontcountry – visitor concentration

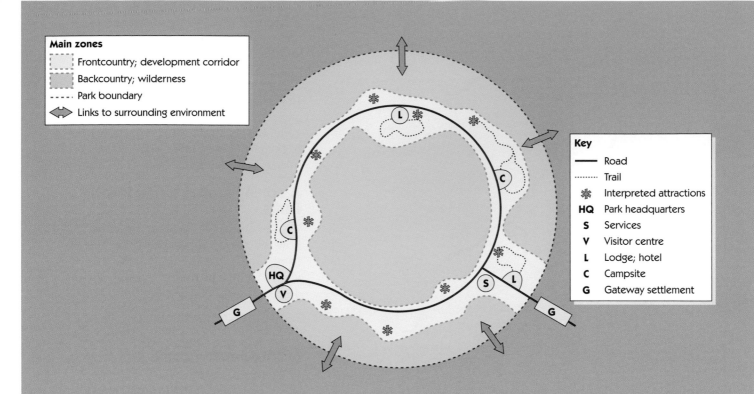

Main zones
- Frontcountry; development corridor
- Backcountry; wilderness
- ---- Park boundary
- Links to surrounding environment

Key
- —— Road
- .... Trail
- ✳ Interpreted attractions
- HQ Park headquarters
- S Services
- V Visitor centre
- L Lodge; hotel
- C Campsite
- G Gateway settlement

Frontcountry features

- An access corridor which links selected attractive sites and facilities.

- Built facilities are located here.

- Contains environments which are relatively resistant to visitor use.

- The natural environment is modified in order to increase the visitor carrying capacity.

- Managed to concentrate visitors at medium to high densities.

- Strong controls on where people go, and guidance about what they are seeing.

- Must be narrow enough in places to allow wildlife to move freely through the backcountry.

Backcountry features

- Protection by remoteness and limited access; vehicles usually banned.

- Few developed facilities.

- Contains fragile environments with high conservation value.

- Little modification of the natural environment; only low levels of impacts are acceptable.

- Managed for dispersed visitor use at low densities.

- Few obvious controls on visitor movements but strong guidelines on how they should behave.

- Must be large enough to allow the ecosystems to be sustained over time

Figure H   A two-zone model for National Parks

Building developments are strictly controlled but many parks have one or more hotels or lodges. The hotel in Figure I, at Lake Louise, Jasper National Park, Alberta, Canada, is one of the largest. Some parks are trying to remove large facilities and park headquarters to locations outside the park, e.g. to 'gateway' settlements.

Backcountry Zone

Access to the backcountry or wilderness is from trailheads, where you leave your car. You buy a wilderness permit from the park Visitor Centre. Only so many permits are available, in order to control visitor numbers and where they go.

Figure I The frontcountry – Lake Louise Hotel, Jasper National Par

Figure J The backcountry – visitor dispersion. At this trailhead, in Saguaro National Park, Arizona, a runner and a backpacker swap stories.

▼ Questions

14 Give two ways in which park managers have increased the carrying capacity of the frontcountry zone.

15 Explain how the frontcountry zone helps in the conservation of the backcountry environment.

16 Using Figures F, G, H, I and J suggest how park managers try to provide enjoyable experiences for each type of visitor in Figure E, and still achieve a park's conservation aims. ➡

Measuring sustainability

Main activity

A technique for measuring the environment.

How do we know that it's working?

Most management plans claim that one of their aims is to sustain the environment by balancing conservation and development. Once the plan is in operation, the managers face a tricky question: 'How do we know whether we are achieving our aim?' One method is to use a set of indicators. An indicator measures the character or condition of a part of the environment, for example, water quality, number of trees per hectare or % of houses with double glazing. If we take measurements of these indicators over time, we can follow changes in the environment. This type of information is called time series data. We can then compare this data with what our management plan says the environment should be like (Figure A).

	Question	Response	
Stage 1	What is it like now?	Measure and record the character and condition of the environment.	= ENVIRONMENTAL AUDIT
Stage 2	What do we want it to be like in the future?	The character and condition of the environment to be sustained by the plan.	= ENVIRONMENTAL FORECAST
Stage 3	How can we measure what is happening?	Identify indicators to measure environmental changes.	= ENVIRONMENTAL MEASUREMENT
Stage 4	Are we achieving our aims?	Measure and record what is happening to the environment.	= ENVIRONMENTAL MONITORING
Stage 5	What do we need to do?	Respond to changes identified by the indicator measurements.	= MANAGEMENT STRATEGY

Figure A   Some questions and answers for managers

The case study which follows shows how this approach is being developed for use in the Cairngorm Mountains of Scotland. Here, a new management plan hopes to settle conflicts about how this beautiful but fragile region should be used. The goal of the plan is to sustain the regional environment and economy. The set of indicators set out in this case study will be used to monitor (keep a check on) whether this goal is being achieved. Notice that the choice of indicators depends on:
● The type of environment.
● The aims of the plan.
● How the information can be obtained.
● How the data is to be stored and used.

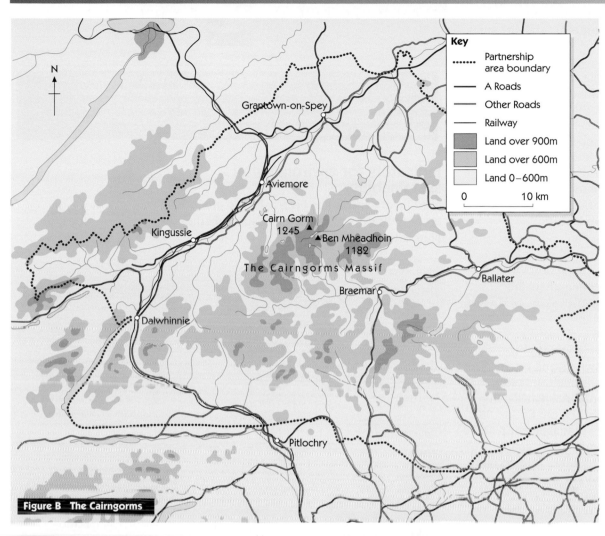

Figure B The Cairngorms

Key
- .... Partnership area boundary
- ——— A Roads
- ——— Other Roads
- ——— Railway
- Land over 900m
- Land over 600m
- Land 0–600m

0   10 km

Grantown-on-Spey
Aviemore
Kingussie
Cairn Gorm 1245 ▲
▲ Ben Mheadhoin 1182
The Cairngorms Massif
Ballater
Braemar
Dalwhinnie
Pitlochry

The environment

The Cairngorms include some of the highest and remotest areas of the United Kingdom (Figure B). They contain environments of great beauty and very high conservation value (Figures C and D). Population densities are low but the resources are used in a number of ways and the Cairngorm environment is under threat.

The Cairngorms do not have National Park status, but have been proposed as a World Heritage Site. This indicates their very high conservation value.

Figure C The high plateau surfaces form the most southerly European outpost of a sub-arctic ecosystem. This rare and fragile environment takes a long time to recover when it is damaged.

Figure D The straths and glens (valleys) contain the finest fragments of the great Caledonian forest which once covered much of Scotland. These woodlands have high conservation value but are threatened by deer grazing, farming and the growth of tourism.

The issues

Eleanor Lothian's family farm lies on the southern slopes of the mountains, and she sums up some of the issues:

'The problem is that people want to use the Cairngorms in so many different ways. There's farming, forestry, the big estates with their deer-stalking, grouse shooting and sport fishing. Then there's all sorts of recreation and tourism, from skiing and climbing through coach tours to bird-watching. In addition there are the environmentalists who see the Cairngorms as Britain's last great wilderness, where precious natural ecosystems must be conserved. So, the conflicts roll on: my family and other local people have to make a living; visitors want to enjoy themselves; environmentalists are obsessed with conservation.'

The response

Because of the variety of owners and interests, decision-making has been difficult. In 1995, the government set up the Cairngorms Partnership which is run by a committee (Figure E). In 1997 the Partnership published a management plan for the 50,000 ha area (Figure B). Its goal of environmental sustainability takes into account:
- the area's conservation value;
- its importance for recreation;
- the need to sustain the region's economy and the social life of local communities.

Figure E The Partnership brings people together, in meetings and conferences, privately and in public, to develop common ideas and put them into action. Scottish National Heritage (a government agency) are key partners, along with local authorities, government departments, voluntary organisations, landowners, local communities and businesses.

Indicators for environmental sustainability

A group of experts has been asked to produce a set of indicators which can measure whether the plan is working (Figure F).

Indicators	Measures	
Natural environment	Examples of environmental condition	Examples of socio-economic pressures
Woodlands	Species diversity	Stock of trees
Wetlands	Bird numbers; water quality	Area drained or reclaimed; level of recreational use
Red deer	Population; habitat condition	People paying to shoot; numbers of deer shot
Human environment		
Economy	Area lost to development	Population change; changes in jobs
Housing	Built-up area	Number of new houses
Recreation	Length of footpaths; extent of footpath erosion	Tourist accommodation; number of visitors

Figure F   Some indicators for environmental sustainability

▼ Questions

1   Look again at Figure D.
   a   Suggest one reason for the selection of woodlands as an indicator (Figure F).
   b   Explain how the data from the measures given would help managers to monitor sustainability of the woodland.
   c   Suggest one other measure which might be useful for measuring woodland sustainability.
   d   Give one other indicator and measure which could be related to trends in woodland. Explain briefly what this relationship might be.
2   Select one indicator from the human component of the list (Figure F). Answer a–d as in question 1, replacing 'woodland' with the indicator you have chosen.

Review

- The Cairngorm Partnership brings together the various owners and interest groups for the first time. This should help decision-making.
- The Partnership area covers 500,000 ha which have high conservation value.
- Management plans need to be based on identifying the valued features of an environment and the pressures upon those features.
- Environmental managers need to know whether their plans are succeeding.
- Sets of indicators can be useful in measuring what is happening to an environment.
- Managers can use the measurements from indicators to adjust their plans.

Environments – who should make the decisions?

Key ideas

● Ownership has different meanings in different societies.
● Ownership brings responsibilities as well as rights.
● Where an environment has both high conservation and economic values, there is likely to be conflict between different interest groups.
● Short-term economic benefits may threaten long-term environmental sustainability.

Main activity

Decision-making.

Do you know?

? Non-renewable resources, once they are used, cannot be restored or renewed.
? Large deposits of uranium ore are found in only a few locations.
? Uranium is a key raw material used in generating nuclear energy.
? Water moves through a drainage basin by surface and groundwater flows.
? Polluted or contaminated water contains materials that harm living organisms. Humans are often the cause of water pollution.

Thinking about sustainability

In the case studies throughout this book, we have been asking questions about environments (Figure A). Many have focused on whether a particular environment is being used and managed sustainably. That is, will its qualities be sustained over time? We have seen that this is controlled by the values and priorities of those with the power to influence decisions.

What is the environment like?

How is the environment changing?

What is happening to it?

Who should decide what is to happen?

Why is it happening?

Who decides what is happening?

Figure A   Key questions about environments

Ownership is one crucial element. Owners may be individuals or collectives, such as communities, the State, companies, organisations. The idea of individual ownership is unknown in many traditional societies. They believe they belong to the environment just as much as the environment belongs to them, communally. We often say that such societies 'live in harmony' with their environment, and that their way of life is environmentally sustainable. The Aboriginal peoples of Australia illustrate this people–environment relationship vividly. They believe that powerful spirits which guide and control their lives, inhabit the land, water and skies around them. The environment, therefore, is sacred (Figure B).

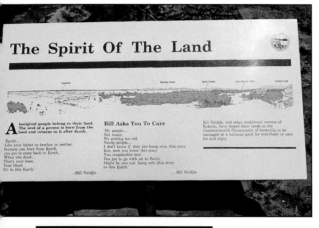

Figure B   To the Aboriginal people the environment is sacred

But life for the Aborigines, as for traditional societies all over the world, has changed. First, much of their land has been taken from them. Second, they see how the resources of these traditional lands have made the new owners wealthy. Not surprisingly, they feel they have the right to exploit the resources that still belong to them.

The following case study, from the Kakadu region of northern Australia, shows that twin dangers may emerge:

● The traditional owners may lose control to outside business and conservation interests.
● The use of the resources may bring economic profits in the short-term, but may cause long-term environmental damage.

Two issues then arise:

● Do governments and outside interest groups such as environmentalists have the right to decide what is to happen?
● Do owners have responsibilities to act as caring stewards of the environment as well as the rights to exploit the environment?

CASE STUDY: Kakadu National Park, Australia

The environment

Kakadu National Park covers about 20,000 square kilometres. across Australia's 'Top End' (Figure C). It is also a World Heritage Site, one of the few designated for both natural and cultural qualities. It has a very high conservation value.

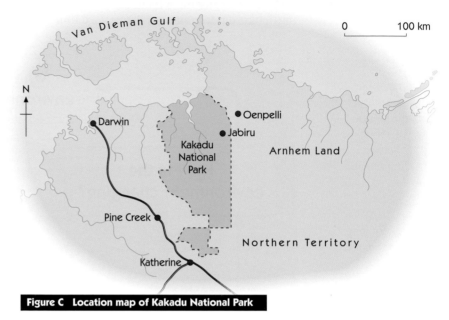

Figure C   Location map of Kakadu National Park

Aboriginal peoples have lived here for at least 50,000 years, and the park contains some of the finest rock artwork in the world. When Europeans first arrived nearly 200 years ago there were at least 3,000 Aborigines living in scattered bands. Today there are fewer than 500.

Today's non-aboriginal population see the tropical monsoon climate as having two seasons, 'The Wet' and 'The Dry'. The mean annual rainfall is 1,600 mm, with over 80% falling in the wet season between October and March. Daytime temperatures reach 30°C in every month. The Aboriginal people see their year quite differently (Figure D). This is an example of the close and spiritual relationship with their environment.

Figure D   The Aboriginal Year

Kakadu has several distinct physical and ecological environments (Figure E). The region is drained by the north-flowing Alligator River system. The wetlands have the greatest variety of species (biodiversity) and the highest conservation value (Figure F). These, and the mangrove forests fringing the coast are particularly sensitive to changes in water quality.

Figure E   Artist's impression of Kakadu environments

Figure F   The Anbangbang billabong. In the wet season the water level rises to the edge of the woodland. This scene is late in the hot, dry season. Many species of water birds gather here each day.

Tourism and the National Park

In 1996, approximately 250,000 tourists visited the park. They bring more than $AUS 60 million a year into the regional economy. The visitors fall into three main groups:
- coach parties on day trips from Darwin, the capital and main town of Northern Territory;
- people travelling by coach or car and who stay at lodges in the park;
- adventure tourists who camp and tour the more remote areas of the park in four-wheel drive vehicles (Figure G).

Figure G   Adventure tourism – penetrating the outback

The main attractions are the remote and natural landscape, the wildlife of the wetlands and the aboriginal rock art. Visitor numbers are growing and are making conservation management difficult at the more popular sites. Maintaining a high quality environment is vital if tourism is to remain successful. In 1997 a new management plan for the park was introduced.

Conservation aims of the new plan for Kakadu National Park

- To conserve the main environments of the park, especially the wetlands and their wildlife.
- To protect aboriginal sacred sites from intrusion.
- To limit the numbers of visitors to the most popular rock art sites, rivers and billabongs.
- To control the number of off-road vehicles in the remote 'bush' or backcountry.

Uranium mining in the Kakadu region

In 1978, the aboriginal owners of this region made two agreements. The first was with the government to lease land for the establishment of a National Park. The second was to lease a section of land to a mining company to exploit valuable uranium ore deposits (Figure H). The mining lease lies entirely surrounded by National Park land (Figure I).

Figure H   This sign marks the boundary between the National Park and the uranium mining lease

IF YOU DEPART FROM OENPELLI ROAD, YOU ARE ENTERING ABORIGINAL LAND WHICH IS THE SUBJECT OF A MINERAL LEASE.

IT IS AN OFFENCE TO ENTER ABORIGINAL LAND WITHOUT A PERMIT

GO BACK TO OENPELLI ROAD UNLESS YOU HOLD A VALID PERMIT.

PERMITS MUST BE PRESENTED ON REQUEST BY ANY POLICE OFFICER.

Figure I   Mining leases and the environment

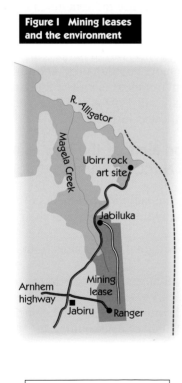

Key
- - - - - National Park boundary

▨ Wetlands

───── Road

═════ New road

Uranium ore has been extracted from the Ranger mine since 1980. The mine consists of three open-cast pits, a processing mill, large mounds of waste materials (tailings) and storage ponds for contaminated water.

The new town of Jabiru has been created to house and service the mining population and has also become the centre of the tourist industry (1996 population 1,500). Like other minerals, uranium is a non-renewable resource, and the deposits at Ranger will run out within the next few years. For this reason, the mining company, Energy Resources of Australia (ERA), want to open up a new deposit at Jabiluka, 20 km to the north (Figure I). Environmentalists and supporters of the National Park have always opposed the mining, and are campaigning strongly against the Jabiluka project.

Uranium mining – the case for

Ross Stewart (Mining engineer):
'These ten points support our case:'

● The uranium from Jabiluka will bring up to $AUS 3.8 billion to the Australian economy.
● By extending the life of mining in the region, Jabiluka will be worth up to $AUS 200 million in royalties (fees for the rights to mine) to the local communities, particularly the aborigines.
● Mining provides 37% of local jobs. The new mine will support up to 130 jobs. We will give priority to the aborigines.
● The mine at Jabiluka will be underground. There will be no processing or large waste dumps.
● There will be no mining in the National Park. The mine will not be visible from the park.
● A special 22 km road will be built to take the rock ore by lorry to the processing mill at Ranger. Waste rock will be returned to fill the mine at Jabiluka.
● No aboriginal sacred sites will be affected and there are no aboriginal camps within 3.5 km of the road.
● The Jabiluka mine has been designed to keep poor quality water within the mine area. There will be no release of low quality water into the local streams. When mining ends after 28 years, the landscape will be returned to its original character.
● Without mining, there will be less money and fewer people in the region. This would make the provision of community services difficult. Even the tourism industry would suffer because an aboriginal corporation runs the main hotel and lodges.
● At the Ranger site our estimates show that we can store the tailings and the contaminated water. Acceptable quality water will be released into the river basin.

Figure J The Jabiluka mine and road will lie in the woodland beyond the wetland. In this open landscape the noise and dust from the mine and lorries will be heard and seen over great distances.

Jabiluka and Ranger – the case against

● Richard Ledgar (Scientist with the Australian Conservation Foundation (ACF)):

'We agree that the Jabiluka mine will have less environmental impact than Ranger. The mine will be underground and there will be no on-site processing. On the other hand, the new road will cut through an undisturbed area.'

● The system may not work. Processing uranium ore produces large volumes of waste rock – the tailings. At Ranger the tailings are dumped in a storage pit. ERA plan to process the Jabiluka ore at the Ranger mill. These tailings will then be stored in the disused Ranger pit. The tailings have to be stored on-site because they contain toxic and radioactive materials.

Runoff and seepages from heavy rains wash out toxic materials from the tailings. The company must retain this contaminated water within a limited area, called the Restricted Release Zone (RRZ).

● The problem is about water seepage and releases. Disused mining pits are where most of the contaminated water is stored. There is then slow groundwater flow into the river basins. However, the company plans to fill these pits with tailings. This will reduce the volume of water that can be stored in the RRZ. Already, in two very wet years, contaminated floodwaters have poured into the rivers. In 1995, ERA wanted to release 500,000 cubic metres because the storage pits were full.

● ERA has applied for permission to release more water from the RRZ. So far they have been turned down. The company claims it will create a wetland in the RRZ to act as a filter. Then, more water can be released. The danger of polluted floodwaters entering the river system and the wetlands remains. Also, creatures which would feed and drink from the artificial wetland could carry the contaminants beyond the RRZ. These processes would damage not only the ecosystems but also the profitable tourism industry.

▼ Questions

1. Describe the character of the planned Jabiluka mine and how it will work.
2. Give two reasons why ERA want to develop the Jabiluka mine.
3. What reasons are given by ERA, claiming that there will be few environmental impacts and that Kakadu National Park will not be affected?
4. How will the Jabiluka project benefit the aboriginal population?
5. Outline the differences between the claims of ERA and ACF concerning the impacts of the Jabiluka–Ranger road.
6. Describe how the present policy at Ranger is meant to prevent contaminated water from entering the National Park.
7. Why does ACF believe that the controls on water pollution are not working, and why the Jabiluka project will increase the problem?
8. What does ERA intend to do to be able to release water from Ranger into the West Alligator drainage basin?
9. Aboriginal peoples still own the National Park and mining lease areas. Some groups welcome the money they receive; others believe their sacred lands are being invaded and their traditional way of life destroyed. State briefly what you think about each of the following alternatives:
   a They have agreed to lease the land, they get their money, and have no right to decide what happens.
   b They still own the land and have a right to be involved in partnership with ERA, the National Park managers and environmental groups.
   c It is still their land, and so they have the right to decide. ➡
10. Write a brief report, giving your decision on whether the Jabiluka project should:
    a go ahead as planned;
    b go ahead, but with modifications;
    c be rejected.
    Give reasons supporting your decision. ➡

Review

● The area included within Kakadu National Park is owned by aboriginal peoples, and leased to the National Park managers.
● The aboriginal owners have leased mineral rights for certain sections within the park to a uranium mining company.
● The Ranger mine has been operating for 20 years, and now the company wants to open a new mine at Jabiluka. Some aboriginal communities support the proposal.
● Environmentalists and National Park managers oppose the new mine. They believe it will cause water pollution and damage wildlife.
● This example raises the question of whether owners have responsibilities as well as rights concerning how environmental resources are used.

A

| Acid rain | Precipitation containing pollutants released by the burning of fossil fuels. | 58 |
| Altitude | Angle of elevation above the horizon. | 35 |

B

Biodiversity	The number and variety of species in one area.	31
Biosphere	The zone close to the earth's surface where all life exists.	76
Broads	Shallow lakes formed by the flooding of trenches dug in medieval times for peat.	16

C

| Carrying capacity | The level of use an environment can withstand before levels of impact become unacceptable. | 75 |

D

| Deforestation | The act of cutting down trees in a forest. | 29 |

E

Ecosystem	A system that shows the relationships between a community of living things (plants and animals) and their non-living environment.	29
Eutrophication	The over-enrichment of water by nutrients, leading to an excess of water-plants and animals.	17
Evaporation	The physical process which changes water from a liquid to a gas.	38

H

| Headwater catchment | The upper parts of a drainage basin where headstream tributaries rise. | 45 |
| Hydrosere | The succession of vegetation which evolves in wetlands. | 35 |

I

| Indigenous | A species native to an area or environment. | 29 |

L

Land reform	The redistribution of land ownership and landholding systems.	33
Latitude	Angular distance from the equator.	35
LEDC	Less economically developed country.	36
Location	A place or site.	35

M

| MEDC | More economically developed country. | 36 |
| Model | A simple general representation of a complex reality. | 29 |

N

| National Parks | Areas of great natural beauty where enjoyment of scenery by the public is promoted. | 8 |

P

Percolation	The process by which water moves downwards through soils and rocks.	35
Personal enquiry	Investigation of local issue suitable for use for GCSE course work.	65
Photochemical	Chemical changes brought about by light.	57
Photosynthesis	The process within cells of green plants which uses sunlight to produce oxygen and food molecules.	5

Q

| Quarters | Birmingham city council's plan for the regeneration of the inner city. | 71 |

R

| Resettlement | A process of relocation of people from one place to another. | 32 |

S

Smog (summer)	Atmospheric pollution resulting from the chemical reaction of gases with sunlight. Also know as photochemical pollution.	57
Smog (winter)	Atmospheric pollution consisting of smoke particles, sulphur dioxide and carbon monoxide.	57
Succession	A series of vegetation types following one another in the same region.	16
Sustain	Use a resource without the long term depletion of that resource.	5
Sustainable	A form of use where resources are conserved over time.	7
Symbiotic	A two-way relationship between species or components of an ecosystem.	40

T

Toxic	A poisonous substance which enters an environmental system.	35
Transpiration	The process by which plants lose water through the pores on their leaves.	38
Tundra	A high latitude ecosystem adapted to long, cold, dark waters.	34
Tuscany	One of Italy's twenty regions, situated in the north-west of the country.	26